PRINCIPLES OF SPECIFICATION WRITING

Harold J. Rosen, PE, FCSI
Lecturer in Specifications
School of Architecture,
Pratt Institute

REINHOLD PUBLISHING CORPORATION
A subsidiary of Chapman-Reinhold, Inc.
NEW YORK   AMSTERDAM   LONDON

THIS BOOK
HAS BEEN REVIEWED AND ENDORSED
BY
THE AMERICAN INSTITUTE OF ARCHITECTS

The art of specification writing has progressed immeasurably in recent years, and this advance in the state of the art can be largely attributed to the work of the Construction Specifications Institute and to the Specifications Committee of the American Institute of Architects. For the first time, these professional societies have brought together many individuals having as a common interest, the betterment of specification writing; as a result, there have been discussions of philosophies, an airing of views, and an exploration of facets which have led to the publication of several Standards.

Because no one individual could possibly formulate all of the theories and philosophies presented here, the author has borrowed heavily from such stalwarts as Goldwin Goldsmith, Griffith Edwards, Harold Sleeper, Rolf Retz, Dermot Gale, Donald Watson, and others. This book is a synthesis of the philosophies expressed by these individuals and by the author's own writings which have appeared in *Progressive*

Architecture since 1956 in the column, "Specifications Clinic." It is thus an endeavor to distill ideas from many sources into a set of basic principles that underlie an organic approach to the writing of specifications.

The author wishes to express his appreciation for the time and effort expended by the members of the AIA Committee on Specifications in reviewing the text of this book and for their comments and suggestions. In particular the author is indebted to James C. Hemphill, Jr., and Howard C. Sherman, successive chairmen of the AIA Committee, for their efforts.

The typography, arrangement and style of this book has been designed by Martin Growald R.A., together with Myron Hall of Reinhold Publishing Corporation, and the author is deeply indebted to them for converting a volume of words to a legible text.

This book is dedicated to my wife, Rose Rosen.

Harold J. Rosen

CONTENTS

INTRODUCTION
TO
PRINCIPLES OF SPECIFICATION WRITING

A knowledge of specification writing techniques and the principles of specification writing are essential to the writer in the preparation of sound, enforcible specifications. Unless these skills are properly developed, an expert knowledge of materials, contracts, and construction procedures cannot be communicated successfully to the ultimate users of the finished specifications.

What, then, constitutes the principles of specification writing? Basically, the principles of specification writing should encompass those factors which permit the architect or engineer to understand more clearly the relationship between drawings and specifications, and to enable him to set forth in a logical, orderly sequence the material to be incorporated within a specification.

In broad terms, the principles of specification writing may be set forth as follows:

1. The Role of the Specfications
   Specifications constitute one of the contract documents, together with the drawings and the agreement. Since they are written instructions, they are frequently adjudged by the courts as having greater importance than drawings when these documents are in conflict, and judgments are frequently resolved on the basis of the specifications. Also, the drawings—except for mechanical and electrical drawings—make no attempt at segregating the work of the various trades, and all of the work is shown on them. The specifications, on the other hand, segregate the information depicted on the drawings into the various specification sections, so that a contractor may generally let his subcontracts on the basis of the specification breakdown of sections.

2. The Relationship Between Drawings and Specifications
   Drawings are a graphic portrayal of the work and show size, form, location, and arrangement of the various elements. Specifications should describe the quality of materials, processes, and workmanship. There should not be duplication between these two documents; instead, they should be complimentary. To improve coordination between drawings and specifications, there should be standardization of the information appearing in them.

3. The Organization of Specifications
   For many years, specifications were arranged in a series of

sections based upon the order or chronology in which the various trades appeared on the construction scene. However, it was found that our increasingly complex building structures did not necessarily follow these simple rules, nor was there a uniform, nationwide system of specifications. The recently promulgated "CSI Format for Construction Specifications" has established such a uniform arrangement of division-section organization.

4. The Technical Section and its Arrangement

The technical section, which generally forms a subcontract, must be defined as to its scope and content. The information must then be arranged in an orderly sequence of paragraphs, the heading of each forming a logical and self-explanatory description.

5. Types of Specifications

Specifications can be prepared on the basis of either methods or results. The specifier can elect to specify in detail the method by which a contractor does certain operations in order to achieve a certain result, or, conversely, he can prepare a specification placing upon the contractor the responsibility for securing the desired result, leaving to the contractor the method by which he secures it. Generally, there are four different types of specifications: descriptive, performance, proprietary, and reference.

6. Specification Writing Techniques

These techniques involve the use of scope clauses, the work of other sections, the use of "or equal" or base bid specifications, the avoidance of duplication and repetition, and the use of the residual legatee technique.

7. Specification Language

The use of clear technical language that can be understood by contractors, superintendents, and foremen is imperative. Legal phraseology or highly-stilted formal terms and sentences are to be avoided. Sentences should be clear and concise, and written in simple terms to avoid misunderstanding. Sentence structure, punctuation, and the phraseology used in specification writing is an art in itself.

8. Specification Reference Sources

Knowing where to look for information to be used in specifications is quite important. Materials standards have been established by the Federal Government, the American Society for Testing and Materials, the United States Standards Association, and others. Association standards have been developed by materials manufacturers and subcontractors for materials and workmanship. Many text books on specification writing are available for reference purposes. Guide specifications are available from the American Institute of Architects, and several specification studies are available from the Construction Specifications Institute.

This book is intended as an extension of these principles and is designed for the student as well as a refresher to those currently engaged in writing specifications.

1

THE ROLE OF THE SPECIFICATIONS

Whenever an architect is commissioned by an owner to design a building, he must develop two basic documents which a third party, the contractor, must utilize when he undertakes to build the structure. These two basic documents are the drawings and the specifications; together with the agreement, they constitute the Contract Documents. The American Institute of Architects classifies specifications as one of the Contract Documents—one of the necessary constituent elements of the contract. As one of the major Contract Documents, it is imperative that a practicing architect have a very good working knowledge of the role which specifications play.

Whether the specifications are written by a specification writer in a large office or by the job captain or architect and engineer in a small office, they are utilized by a rather diverse group of participants: They are written for the estimator in the contractor's office, who prepares the estimate based upon the specifications. They are written for the purchasing agent in the contractor's office who will procure the materials and equipment described in the specifications. They are written for the resident project representative or inspector, who must be given a document which will aid him in supervising and directing the work. They are written for the owner, who would like to know what he is buying and what he is entitled to receive. They are written for the subcontractors, so that each can readily discern the scope of his contract. They are written for the manufacturers of building materials and equipment, so that the grade and type are clearly defined with respect to the many variations they may manufacture.

Webster's Unabridged Dictionary gives this definition of the term *specifications:* "Specifications (usually plural)—A written or printed description of work to be done, forming part of the contract and describing qualities of material and mode of construction, and also giving dimensions and other information not shown in the drawings." But the dictionary description will not suffice. As we explore the full meaning of the term, we discover many areas solely within the province of the specifications which extend far beyond a mere elaboration of the drawings.

For example, the specifications alone, as a contract document prepared by the architect, set forth legal requirements, insurance requirements, bidding procedures, alternates, options, subcontractor limits, and inspection and testing procedures. In many instances, design decisions cannot be shown on the drawings, and the specifications are the only vehicle through which these design considerations may be transmitted to the contractor. The following illustrates the function of the specifications:

1. Legal Considerations

a. As a written document, the courts have generally held that in the event of conflict between drawings and specifications, the specifications govern, and judgments are most frequently resolved on the basis of the specification requirements.

b. General Conditions—whether they consist of A.I.A. standard preprinted forms, federal, state, or municipal forms, the Consulting Engineers Council forms, or individually prepared general conditions—are usually bound into the specifications and, by reference, made a part of the specifications. The content and role of the general conditions will be elaborated upon separately. Essentially, however, they establish the legal rights, responsibilities, and relationships of the parties to the contract.

2. Insurance Considerations

Insurance requirements governing workmen's compensation, contractor's liability, and fire insurance are usually incorporated in the general conditions or in supplementary conditions, and again made a part of the specifications by incorporation therein.

3. Bidding Requirements

The bidding requirements include the Invitation to Bid, the Instructions to Bidders, the Bid Form, and the Bid Bond. These bidding requirements are developed by the architect solely for the use of the bidder and are intended to provide the bidder with information required to submit a proposal. These are usually bound in the specifications and made a part thereof.

4. Alternates, Options

a. The specifications provide a basis for the contractor's estimate and the submission of a bid. In the Bid Form, or Form of Proposal, alternates are established by the architect for the deletion of work, the addition of work, and for the substitution of materials.

b. The technical specifications may permit the contractor, at his option, to use one of several materials or manufacturers' brands specified for use in the work.

5. Subcontractor's Limits

Drawings generally show all of the work to be done and the interrelationship of the various parts. No attempt is made on the drawings to segregate the work of the several subcontractors, except that separate drawings are generally prepared for plumbing, heating, ventilating and air conditioning, and electrical work. The specifications segregate the work shown on the drawings into many sections, or units of work, so that the general contractor may sublet the work to various subcontractors.

6. Inspection and Testing Procedures

The specifications establish inspection and testing procedures to be followed during the construction operations. Standards for office and field inspection of materials are described for numerous materials. Test procedures are given for evaluating the performance of completed mechanical installations.

7. Design Criteria

The drawings cannot in some instances be utilized to show or delineate design decisions. For example, the architect's selection of finish hardware for doors can be described only in the specifications. Directions for paint materials, the number of coats of paint, and the degree of luster or sheen are likewise given only in the specifications.

Project Manual

For many years, all of the materials bound together—the invitation to bid, the instructions to bidders, the bid forms, the sample forms of agreements and bonds, and the technical sections—have been known as the Specifications. Actually this is a misnomer, since the bidding requirements and the agreements and bonds are not properly a part of the specifications. In an attempt to clarify this situation, the September 1966 issue of the *AIA Architect's Handbook of Professional Practice,* Chapter 14, introduces a new term to replace the old, and describes its contents and function as follows:

Project Manual Concept—The Project Manual is a reorganized version of the familiar volume commonly called "Specifications". This new title better describes the scope and content and avoids confusion of the bound volume with that part of the Contract Documents called the Specifications. This new concept provides an orderly, systematic arrangement of requirements divided in two basic parts; Bidding Requirements, which govern activities prior to Contract execution, and Contract Documents, which constitute the Contract between the Owner and the Contractor.

The sequence recommended by the AIA for the material to be bound in the Project Manual is as follows:

Title Page
Table of Contents
Addenda (if bound in Project Manual)

Bidding Requirements

Invitation to Bid or Advertisement
Instruction to Bidders
Sample Forms
   Agreement
   Bid Form
   Bid Bond
   Performance and Payment Bonds

Contract Documents

Agreement
Conditions of the Contract
   General Conditions
   Supplementary Conditions
Schedule of Drawings
Technical Specifications

2

RELATIONSHIP BETWEEN
DRAWINGS AND SPECIFICATIONS

The necessary information for the construction of a building is developed by the architect by means of two basic documents, the drawings and the specifications. These two documents represent a means of communication between architect and contractor, but each document uses a special form of communication, one pictorial, the other verbal. Yet, in spite of these distinct methods of transmitting information, the documents should complement one another, and neither overlap nor duplicate. In this way, each documents fulfills its own function. In broad terms, the drawings are a graphic portrayal and the specifications a written description of the legal and technical requirements forming the contract documents. Each should convey its own part of the story completely, and neither should repeat any part that properly belongs to the other, since duplication can very often result in differences of meaning.

Drawings present a picture, or a series of pictures, of the building or parts of a building to be erected. They give the size, form, location, and arrangement of the various elements. This information cannot be described in the specifications, since it is shown by means of lines, dots, and symbols peculiar to drawings. In fact, a drawing is a special language or means of communication to convey ideas of construction from one person to another. These ideas cannot be conveyed by the use of words.

Specifications, on the other hand, describe the quality of materials, processes, and workmanship required to complete a building. Thus, a specification for the structural steel work of a building is a detailed description of the nature and physical characteristics of the steel to be used, the methods of assembling it and raising it into place, and the labor or workmanship required to produce, erect, and finish the work.

Specifications are, by their very nature, a device for organizing the information depicted on the drawings. The drawings show the interrelationship of all the parts that go together to make the grand design. It has only been a relatively short time that mechanical, electrical, and structural information have been shown on separate drawings. All of the general construction details are shown properly on drawings as they relate to one another, with no attempt at separation of diverse materials. It is the specifications that break down the interrelated information shown on drawings into separate, organized, and orderly units of work which we refer to as technical sections of the specifications.

To maintain the separate yet complementary character of these two documents and to ensure that they will be interlocking but not overlapping requires the development of definite systems for each. Hence, what is better described in the specifications should not be shown on the drawings and, likewise, what is better shown on the drawings should not be described in the specifications.

Drawings should generally show the following information:
1. Location of materials, equipment, and fixtures.
2. Detail and over-all dimensions.
3. Interrelation of materials, equipment, and space.
4. Schedules of finishes, windows, and doors.
5. Sizes of equipment.

Specifications should generally describe the following items:
1. Type and quality of materials, equipment, and fixtures.
2. Quality of workmanship.
3. Methods of fabrication, installation, and erection.
4. Test and code requirements.
5. Gages of manufacturers' equipment.

Specifications should not overlap or duplicate information contained on the drawings. Duplication, unless it is repeated exactly word for word, is harmful in that it can lead to contradiction, confusion, misunderstanding, and difference of opinion. Duplication, word for word, is redundant.

To achieve this proper separation of information between drawings and specifications, it is essential that the development of the specifications should go hand in hand with the preparation of the drawings. At the outset, someone in the office should be made responsible for establishing and keeping the all-important checklist for a specific project. This checklist should establish a schedule of what shall appear on the drawings, what shall be described in the specifications, and what is to be itemized and listed in schedules. The checklist should include preliminary or outline specifications, lists of all decisions made in the drafting room, and notes of all changes made on the drawings since the last set was printed for the specifications writer, including questions to be settled.

The broad guide-lines previously noted for the separation of material that appears on the drawings and in the specifications does not go far enough in establishing a line of demarcation between these documents, inasmuch as there are areas of disagreement among authorities on specifications writing as to the specific information that should be shown and / or specified. For example, one authority suggests that the drawings should indicate a material such as concrete and the specifications should determine whether it is to be precast or cast-in-place concrete. It would be preferable that the drawings delineate the location of these two materials. Another authority argues against the customary hatching and other indication of materials on plans and elevations. If the experts disagree, how can the draftsman and the neophyte specifications writer settle the issue? Duplication exists between drawings and specifications for lack of a clear-cut and well-defined policy.

Generally, each office establishes a policy to be followed in its own practice. However, systems can be formulated between the specifications writer and the draftsman, and as a general rule it will follow that common sense will dictate which medium serves as the better means of communication.

3

THE ORGANIZATION
OF SPECIFICATIONS

When the term *Organization of Specifications* is used, it refers to the separation of the specifications into a series or a schedule of separate units of work termed "technical sections." (See Chapter 4 for a definition of the Technical Section.) The history of specification writing and the growth in complexity of buildings illustrates how this system of a series of technical sections has evolved.

Specifications in the Eighteenth and Nineteenth Centuries consisted of a single document containing a description of all of the work and materials to be included in a building. This was especially true of small, simple structures which were constructed by a general contractor who engaged all the crafts and did not sublet or subcontract any parts of the work. An early textbook entitled *Handbook of Specifications,* by T. L. Donaldson, London, 1860, provided for the arrangement of specifications on a craft basis. The specifications were divided into two main general divisions, with subdivisions as follows:

Carcase	**Finishing**
Excavator	Joiner
Bricklayer	Plasterer
Mason	Plumber
Slater	Painter
Founder and Smith	Glazier
Carpenter	Paperhanger
	Ironmonger
	Smith and Bellhanger
	Gasfitter

As materials and methods of construction gained a degree of sophistication, the specification sections began to change with the times and took on additional crafts within one section of the specifications. In lieu of the general contractor hiring specific crafts under his own supervision, he began to sublet portions of the work to subcontractors who, in turn, hired the several crafts to perform certain parts of the work.

Specifications written for buildings toward the end of the Nineteenth Century consisted generally of three main sections—Masonry, Carpentry, and Mechanical Work—with various allied or related subjects under each section. The masonry section included excavation, concrete, brickwork, stonework, steel columns and lintels, and waterproofing. The carpentry section included roofing, glazing, and painting, as well as carpentry. The mechanical or pipe trades consisted of plumbing, gas, and heating work. When electricity came into use, it was included in the mechanical work.

The foregoing arrangement of the specifications was adequate for the nature of the buildings constructed at that time, and for the materials and methods of construction prevalent at that time. However, our buildings grew more complex, our materials and construction techniques more involved; it became necessary to increase the number of sections as more portions of the work came under subcontract. Today, the specification sections are designed essentially to permit general contractors, estimators, subcontractors, manufacturers, and materials dealers to "take off" the items of their work for estimate.

Accuracy in estimating is in the best interests of building owner and architect alike. To assure accuracy, the specifications should be divided into sections so as to permit the builder's estimator and the subcontractors to prepare his estimate quickly and accurately. The preparation of drawings and specifications takes considerable time, while bidding periods are generally of short duration. It is therefore quite evident that the estimator must have a specification so separated by sections or units of work that he can list the materials and quantities, note the methods of their use and installation, separate those parts on which he will take subestimates, secure prices, and tabulate results, all within a three or four week bidding period, and often within only two weeks. Such a system also permits the specification writer to organize his own material. It provides him with a method for organizing the information on the drawings in a systematic, orderly, and prearranged manner.

For convenience in writing, for speed in estimating, and for ease of reference, it has been found that the most suitable organization of the specifications is a series of sections dealing successively with the different subcontractors, and in each section grouping all of the work of the particular trade to which the section is devoted.

Until April 1963, when the "CSI Format for Construction Specifications" was promulgated by the Construction Specifications Institute, each specification writer organized his specifications in a series of sections which more or less followed a time relationship, or chronological order, related to the order-of-appearance on the site of the various subcontractors. However, from office to office, and even within the same office, this order was not uniform. In addition, complex structures required that certain mechanical trades be involved at an early stage in the construction process so that a true trades-chronology was not possible in the organization of the specifications. It became apparent that a major overhaul was required in the organization of specification sections, and that a uniform system would, in addition, provide certain corollary benefits.

The CSI Format for Construction Specifications is as follows:
   Bidding Requirements
   Contract Forms
   General Conditions (and Supplementary Conditions)
   Specifications
      Division 1—General Requirements
      Division 2—Site Work
      Division 3—Concrete
      Division 4—Masonry
      Division 5—Metals; Structural & Miscellaneous
      Division 6—Carpentry
      Division 7—Moisture Protection
      Division 8—Doors, Windows, and Glass
      Division 9—Finishes
      Division 10—Specialties
      Division 11—Equipment
      Division 12—Furnishings
      Division 13—Special Construction
      Division 14—Conveying Systems
      Division 15—Mechanical
      Division 16—Electrical

How does one use this new system? For each specific project, the specification writer prepares his technical sections as he did previously, except that he now places them under the fixed division. (See Chapter 17 for the breakdown of sections under each division.) Where local trade practices or conditions of the specific project dictate, the specification writer has the prerogative to alter the location of the information and the section.

The "CSI Format for Construction Specifications," now much more completely updated by the "Uniform System," is somewhat analogous to the organization of specifications referred to earlier in the *Handbook of Specifications.* The division headings under the CSI Format are based upon four major categories—materials, trades, functions of work, and place relationships. For example, *Division 4, Masonry* is an instance of a materials relationship. The sections listed under Division 4 have as their common denominator, materials. These include sections on unit masonry, stone, mortar and masonry restoration, all dealing with materials common to one another. *Division 5, Metals; Structural and Miscellaneous* is an example of a trades relationship. Sections on structural metal, open-web joists, metal decking, miscellaneous metal, and ornamental metal, are located here, and the metal fabricators, erectors, and ironworkers usually perform this type of work. *Division 7, Moisture Protection* is illustrative of a relationship based on function of work. The sections dealing with the environmental protection of the building are located here: roofing, waterproofing, dampproofing, thermal insulation, caulking and sealing. *Division 2, Site Work* is an example of a place relationship and includes such sections as demolition, clearing and grubbing, earthwork, piling, roads and walks, and lawns and planting.

What are the advantages of this particular system for organizing the specifications? In preparing his specification section, the specifier need no longer be concerned with whether the architect or the engineer adds or deletes certain materials or trades as he develops his drawings. Previously, this change in design meant the deletion of a specification section or the inclusion at the last moment of a specification section placed entirely out of sequence. Under the "Uniform System," such revisions do not impose hardships, since a section can be added to or deleted from a specific division without radically upsetting a numbering system. The specifier can write or prepare sections long before the drawings are completed and assign numbers to them immediately. In addition, the specification writer can now file material, shop drawings, correspondence, technical data, literature, samples, estimates, and a host of office memoranda under a similar numbering system. The contractor, manufacturer, estimator, and inspector can find more readily those items in the specifications with which he is concerned.

In time, with widespread use, the AIA will conform its Specification Work Sheets and its Standard Filing System to this system. The Associated General Contractors can number its Estimating Work Sheets on the same basis; Sweet's Catalog Service can renumber its Architectural File; and building materials manufacturers can number their literature accordingly. (See Chapter 17 for a more complete review of the interrelationship of specification sections, data and literature filing, and contractors' estimates.)

4

THE TECHNICAL SECTION

The technical section is a unit of work consisting of a carefully worded description of materials and an explanation of methods of construction in the form of instructions to a contractor. The term *trade section* has been used frequently heretofore to describe this unit; however, under today's connotations and definitions, "trade section" is misleading, and much misunderstanding has arisen from the use of that term as it relates to the technical sections of specifications.

It has previously been pointed out that the drawings generally show all the work that is to be constructed. The only attempt made in the drawings at segregating the work of different "trades" is in the preparation of separate drawings for plumbing, heating, electrical work, and structural work. When a specification is written, the specifier endeavors to segregate under the various technical or trade sections of the specifications a unit of work that a contractor may let to a subcontractor, a unit of work that a materials man may supply for another to install, a unit of work that combines the responsibilities of several subcontractors into a single authority, or a unit of work that is performed by a single recognized trade.

The misunderstanding concerning the use of the word *trade* arises both from the dictionary definition of the word and from the failure to recognize that the so-called trade section of the specifications can be as restrictive or as all-inclusive as previously described. The dictionary defines trade as: "(1) The business one practices or the work in which one engages regularly; occupation; means of livelihood. (2) A pursuit requiring manual or mechanical training and dexterity; a craft. (3) Those engaged in a business or industry." The word trade can therefore mean a craft, such as carpentry, brick laying, or plumbing; or it can mean a business, such as a concrete subcontractor or a plumbing and heating subcontractor.

A unit of work that a contractor may let to a subcontractor can encompass a section entitled "concrete work." The concrete subcontractor employs carpenters for erecting formwork; lathers or ironworkers for installing the steel reinforcement; concrete laborers for placing concrete; and cement masons for finishing the concrete.

A unit of work that a materials man may supply for another to install is exemplified by the section entitled "finish hardware." The general contractor will purchase the hardware from a materials supplier who will simply deliver the material to the site for the carpentry subcontractor to install, or for the general contractor to install with his own forces.

A unit of work that combines several subcontractors so that a single responsibility is established for that portion of the work is illustrated by the section entitled "curtain walls." The general contractor may award this work to one subcontractor who in turn will sublet such items of work as fabrication and installation of metal framing and metal panels, furnishing and installation of glass, caulking and sealing of the curtain wall, flashing of the curtain wall, and insulation of the curtain wall.

A unit of work that is performed by a single recognized trade can best be illustrated by the section entitled "painting." While the work may be done by a subcontractor who employs only painters, the general contractor may elect to hire his own painting crew to perform this portion of the work.

It is not a simple matter to determine the proper subdivision of the technical sections, and once made it is not necessarily permanent. Changes will occur as new materials are introduced by building materials manufacturers, and recognized trades will change as a result of these new materials. Changes will also occur as new concepts in design appear, such as the curtain wall and the integrated ceiling. Changes will also be dictated by the introduction of new construction techniques, such as lift slabs and slip forming. Concrete work was formerly a general mason's work; now it is specified under "concrete division" and performed by a concrete subcontractor. Wood forms for concrete work were once specified under Carpentry, but are now specified under concrete work. As new methods of work develop, they are at first performed by an existing craft, but eventually come under the jurisdiction of specialty subcontractors where new skills must be developed.

The technical section can vary in size or scope according to the specific project. The concrete section for a non-fireproof dwelling will be small in scope and the descriptive material brief; however, it will still be necessary to write this section as a unit of work to be let as a subcontract. For a high-rise fireproof structure, the concrete section will encompass many aspects of concrete work—admixtures, testing, hot and cold weather concreting, concrete finishes, form removal—and this technical section will be relatively long and involved.

There is, however, another criterion to be considered in determining whether a long, involved concrete section should be written as a single unit of work. Is the amount of work so large in scope and its dollar value so high that it becomes too unmanageable and out of the reach of a subcontractor? In this case, consideration should be given to establishing several technical sections involving certain units of work that may be subcontracted. The concrete reinforcement in a very large project may be established as a technical section. In addition, the concrete form work, the concrete testing and the purchase of ready-mix concrete may be established as separate units of work within their respective technical sections.

In establishing the technical sections for a project, the specification writer should assume that the general contractor may desire to sublet all of the work, doing nothing himself except to organize and manage the project. If the specification sections are planned on this basis, it will be possible for the general contractor to reserve for himself whatever parts of the work he may be equipped to do, and sublet all of the other parts. It will be quite simple for him to sublet two or more sections to one subcontractor if the work is broken down into small units of work, but it would be difficult for him to divide certain parts of the work between two subcontractors, if these parts are not properly separated in the specifications.

It is generally true that a large number of smaller units of work will simplify the work of the estimator, make it easier for the superintendent to refer to the specifications for any particular part of the work, and aid the specifier in his note-taking for writing of the section. It is also necessary to point up the fact that there are certain instances where the work is so closely united in execution as to be combined in one technical section to simplify handling and to place a combination of two or more subcontracts on the shoulders of one subcontractor, who may then sublet part of the work. The curtain wall, the integrated ceiling, roofing, and sheet metal work are examples of composite construction which dictate broader technical sections.

However, the specification writer should not lose sight of the fact that although he may establish the technical sections with the scope of each as limited or as broad as he may elect, it is still the privilege of the general contractor to combine or distribute the various technical sections in any manner he wishes, or to use them and let them as written. The general conditions of the contract should be implemented with the following admonition:

> The following technical sections are generally divided into units of work for the purpose of ready reference. The division of the work among his subcontractors is the Contractor's responsibility and the architect assumes no responsibility to act as arbiter to establish subcontract limits between any sections of the work.

It should be apparent by now that the scope, content, and nature of the technical section must be flexible. Sections within the same project may be long and involved, yet others may be short and still represent a large percentage of the work. Conversely, their length and content may vary from project to project, and fixed rules for size and content cannot be established. The specifier must thus assess each project on the merits of its own peculiarities and requirements before establishing the scope and content of the individual technical sections.

In order to arrive at more uniform practices nationwide, the Construction Specifications Institute, the AIA and others have published a list of preferred section titles to be used under the respective division headings of the CSI Format. These section titles have been established on the basis of broad section titles and restrictive section titles, following the concept that a technical section may be written as to be all inclusive or restricted as to scope, depending upon the particular project. This arrangement provides the flexibility needed by the specification writer to retain the prerogative of organizing his specifications, while at the same time establishing a uniform system of preferred section titles throughout the profession. (See Chapter 17 for a detailed discussion of this subject.)

ARRANGEMENT OF THE
TECHNICAL SECTION

The arrangement of the subject matter in an orderly, comprehensive format within a technical section is important for several reasons. The specifier, in following a definitive procedure, is less likely to overlook any item. The contractor, estimator, materials manufacturer and inspector will find the information much more readily in the individual section.

A technical section in a book of specifications may be considered as analogous to a chapter in a book; the chapter, in turn, consists of paragraphs. The material that comprises the section consists essentially of paragraphs and subparagraphs. Other names to describe the breakdown of the material within the technical section—such as articles, clauses, headings, categories or units—may lead to confusion. The American Institute of Architects recommends the following classifications: division, section, article, paragraph, subparagraph, and item, for sequence and terminology.

The technical section contains two categories of paragraphs—namely, the technical and nontechnical—as follows:

Technical	Nontechnical
Materials	Scope of Work
Fabrication	Delivery of Materials
Workmanship	Samples and Shop Drawings
Installation	Permits
Tests	Guarantees
Schedules	Cleaning

In arranging for a logical order of paragraphs under a technical section, both the technical and the nontechnical should be presented as they occur chronologically, *i.e.*, in a sequence in which the contractor would ordinarily do his work, and each paragraph heading should be simple and self-explanatory. If the specifier follows this course, he is less likely to omit something, and his reliance upon a check list at his side diminishes accordingly. The following arrangement is suggested in general (there are always exceptions to the rule) for the orderly, chronological make-up of the technical section:

1. General. Make reference to the contract documents as being part of the requirements of this section of the work.
2. Scope of Work. Describe briefly or in detail (whichever method the specifier elects) the scope of the work of the section.
3. Work of Other Sections. Describe those items normally part

of this section which the specifier has for one reason or another specified elsewhere. Do not list items that are not normally the work of this section.

4. Materials. Specify the materials to be used. Reference standards can be noted briefly, *e.g.,* Structural Steel—ASTM A-36.

5. Samples. Require submission of samples for approval. List item, size, and quantity.

6. Shop Drawings. State precisely what is required for approval and scale of drawings.

7. Tests. Tests of individual components such as cement, mortar, concrete, and brick. (Tests of completed systems and installed work are specified later.)

8. General Requirements. This paragraph may include subparagraphs as follows:
   a.   Delivery and storage of materials
   b.   Weather conditions
   c.   Building codes, applicable industry standards
   d.   Field measurements
   Note: If any of these subparagraphs is a major item for a specific section, make it a major paragraph.

9. Fabrication and Manufacturing. Describe shop fabrication of preassembled items.

10. Installation, Application, and Erection.
   a. Preparation of surfaces
   b. Reference to existing conditions
   c. Details of installation
   d. Construction methods
   e. Workmanship

11. Tests of Completed Installation. Include test of mechanical systems, piles, structural elements.

12. Protection and Cleaning.

13. Guarantee. Use only if standard one-year guarantee is extended for this section.

14. Measurement and Payment. Use only where unit prices are involved. It is not required for lump-sum bids.

15. Schedules. Useful for hardware, lighting fixtures, painting, plumbing fixtures.

Do not use these paragraph headings when they do not apply. Introduce new paragraph headings when applicable. Deviations are proper when awkwardness would result from too close an adherence to this rule.

There are basically two types of sections that describe work to be done. One is an on-site manufacturing and installation procedure, the other is an off-site manufacturing and fabrication process with on-site installation. Each procedure will establish the format and the arrangement of the technical section.

Concrete, plastering, masonry, built-up roofing, and terrazzo are examples of the on-site manufacturing process. After the basic materials are delivered to the site, the craftsman must perform many operations involved with mixing, placing, installation, and workmanship. Here the emphasis is on Paragraph 10, Installation, Application and Erection. This paragraph may be expanded as necessary into many major paragraphs, each with its own heading to describe the various operations involved. Note that Paragraph 9, Fabrication and Manufacturing, does not generally apply to technical sections involved in on-site manufacture.

Examples of off-site manufacturing processes as related to technical sections are those connected with factory fabrication and, in some instances, prefinishing of such items as toilet partitions, doors, windows, and miscellaneous equipment and specialties. These sections may require expansion of the descriptive paragraphs under Paragraph 9, Fabrication and Manufacturing, in order to explain more fully these processes. Paragraph 10, Installation, Application and Erection, may in some instances be quite brief for these sections.

In addition to the arrangement suggested hereinbefore for the Section format, the AIA has formulated criteria for organizing the material within the technical Section, and in the *1966 Handbook of Professional Practice,* Chapter 14, suggests this Section Format:

> **SECTION FORMAT** There are certain basic principles to be observed in the preparation of each specification Section. The principle that each and every item of work or material included in the project should be described somewhere in the specifications, and in only one place, is a sound one. However, once the required Sections have been determined and a decision reached as to where each element is to be included, a consistent policy for the format of every Section should be adopted.

> Unless the client prescribes a format precluding it, each Section should be organized as outlined below.

Scope of This Section
- Furnish and Install:
- Furnish for Installation by Owner, Contractor, etc.:
- Furnished by Owner, Contractor, etc., for Installation under this Section:
- Not Included:

General Provisions, including
- Notes
- Prior Approvals
- Industry Standards
- Quality Control
- Shop Drawings
- Samples
- Testing
- Delivery and Storage

Materials, including
- Acceptable Manufacturers
- Substitutions
- Material Specifications

Performance, including
- Fabrication
- Installation

Protection and Cleaning

Closeout, including
- Guaranties and Warranties
- Maintenance and Operating Instructions

Schedules (if required)

It is well to preface each Section in Divisions 2 through 16 with the statement, "Requirements of the Conditions of the Contract and of Division 1 of these Specifications apply to all work under this Section." This principle has important legal significance, as many sub-contracts are based upon a certain Section or Sections of the Specifications, and this cross-reference may be the only instrument by which certain provisions of the Conditions of the Contract and Division 1 are made part of and applicable to each of these subcontracts.

Following "Scope," each Section should contain Articles listing appropriate reference standards governing materials to be used, their fabrication and installation, and inspection and testing requirements applicable to the work covered by the Section. Articles should also be included setting forth instructions for any cutting, patching and cleaning up considered especially applicable.

6

TYPES OF SPECIFICATIONS

In general, there are two basic approaches to the writing of specifications: the method system and the results system. When the method system is employed, the specifier describes in detail the materials, workmanship, installation, and erection procedures to be used by the contractor in the conduct of his work operations in order to achieve the results expected. When the specifier instead elects to specify results, he places upon the contractor the responsibility for securing the desired results by whatever methods the contractor chooses to use.

The method system can best be described as a "descriptive" specification; the results system is best described as a "performance" specification. An appropriate analogy may be made by comparing these approaches with building code standards: The "specifications code" sets forth specific materials and methods that are permitted under the law in the construction of a building. Under the "performance code," materials and methods are left to the architect and engineer, provided that performance criteria for fire protection, structural adequacy, and sanitation are met. As a matter of fact, both the descriptive specification and the performance specification may be used together in the same specification, each in its proper place, in order to achieve the prime objective.

Descriptive Specifications

A descriptive specification can be defined as one that describes in detail the materials to be used, and the workmanship required to fabricate, erect, and install the materials. As an example, a descriptive specification for a masonry wall would describe the materials to be used: the brick and mortar ingredients, the composition of the mortar, tests of individual components, weather conditions during erection, workmanship involved in laying up the brick, type of brick bond, jointing, and finally, the cleaning procedures. This allows all those concerned with specifications an opportunity to check each of the items specified. The supplier furnishes the brick and mortar as specified; the laboratory tests the components in accordance with specified test requirements; the inspector checks the workmanship requirements so carefully specified. If the specifications have been accurately prepared, the masonry wall is erected, accordingly, and the result the architect envisioned has been achieved through his minute description.

Performance Specifications

Performance specifications can be defined as specifying end results by formulating the criteria for its accomplishment. As an example, in a performance specification for a paint material,

43

the end result is obtained by specifying or formulating the following criteria:

1. The painted surface shall withstand 10 washings with a mild detergent.
2. The painted surface shall show no sign of alligatoring or crazing.
3. The painted surface shall be resistant to abrasion when using the Taber Abrasive Method.
4. The painted surface shall have an eggshell finish.

Another example of a performance specification is one for a complete installation of a heating system. The specification spells out these performance requirements:

1. The heating plant shall be capable of providing an interior temperature of 70°F when the outside temperature is 0°F.
2. The heating system shall utilize No. 6 oil and shall be a hot-water system.
3. The heating elements shall be fin-type baseboard radiation.
4. Controls such as thermostats, aquastats, and other safety devices shall be provided to regulate heat and prevent explosion.

Reference Specifications

The reference specification is one which makes reference to a standard that has been established for either a material, a test method, or an installation procedure. These standards likewise are predicated either on descriptive or performance criteria. Several reference standards are illustrated at the end of this chapter.

Before the advent of materials standards such as ASTM Specifications or Federal Specifications, materials were minutely described in the specifications so that the contractor was completely cognizant of what the specifier wanted. In many instances, these descriptive specifications for materials have been supplanted by the aforementioned standards. For example, in lieu of describing portland cement in detail, as to quality, fineness module, and other characteristics, the specifier now simply states that Portland Cement ''shall conform to the requirements of ASTM Specification C-150, Type ___.'' This method of specifying has resulted in a type of specification that can best be described as a reference specification. By making reference to a standard, the standard becomes a part of the specification to the same degree as descriptive or performance specification language is used.

The term "reference specifications" can likewise be applied to workmanship standards. Various trade associations, such as the Tile Council of America, The Gypsum Association, the Painting and Decorating Contractors of America, and others, such as the United States Standards Association, have prepared standard workmanship specifications—for ceramic tile; for furring, lathing, and plastering; for painting, etc.—which can be incorporated by reference in project specifications. By so doing, the detailed, descriptive workmanship clauses for these sections need no longer be copied, but can simply be incorporated into the project specifications by means of the reference method.

The Construction Specifications Institute has a study underway entitled "Reference Workmanship Standards," which is an attempt to prepare workmanship clauses for various sections that can be incorporated in project specifications by reference.

It is essential that the architect and specifier be thoroughly familiar with the standards he incorporates in his specifications. Some standards cover several types and grades, and unless the type or grade is specifically stated, the choice then becomes the contractor's option and not the architect's. In addition, a particular type or grade may be more suited for a particular project so that it should be selected and specified by the architect in preference to another type or grade.

Most standard specifications have been developed by committees representing materials manufacturers, governmental authorities, testing agencies, consumers, and those having a general interest in the particular standard. In many cases these standards are compromises; in some cases only minimum property standards are established; in some instances, it may be necessary to augment or strengthen certain provisions of these standards. This can be done quite readily by modifying the standard. However, one must be certain when modifying a standard that the material can be manufactured or furnished under these modified standards.

All reference specifications used by an architect should be on file in his office. He needs these standards to make certain that the material or the installation procedure he specifies by means of these standards are satisfactory to him and are pertinent to the project. He will need them to check materials and test procedures submitted for his approval. If the architect should elect

45

to use a reference specification for workmanship or for a construction procedure taking place at the site, it will also be necessary for the resident project representative to have a copy of that reference specification, since the detailed requirements are specified in the standard rather than in the basic specification. For example, the architect may refer to an American Concrete Institute Standard for Cold Weather Concreting, which describes procedures for placing concrete in freezing temperatures; or to an ASTM Specification for Masonry Mortar, which describes various materials and mixing proportions of mortar; or to an USA Specification for setting ceramic tile, which describes installation procedures. A simple procedure to insure that the inspector at the site will have the specification reference is to include in the base specifications a provision requiring the contractor to furnish these standards at the same time he makes all his other submittals for approval.

Ceramic Tile for Floors and Walls

A recorded

voluntary recommendation

of the trade published by

the U.S. Department

of Commerce

LLL-I-535
NOVEMBER 7, 1960

SUPERSEDING
Int. Fed. Spec. LLL-F-00321b
July 22, 1955 and
Fed. Spec. LLL-F-321b
June 30, 1942

FEDERAL SPECIFICATION

INSULATION BOARD, THERMAL AND INSULATION BLOCK, THERMAL

This specification was approved by the Commissioner, Federal Supply Service, General Services Administration, for the use of all Federal agencies.

1. SCOPE AND CLASSIFICATION

1.1 Scope.—This specification covers insulating fiberboard for use in building construction.

1.2 Classification.

1.2.1 *Classes and styles.* — Insulating fiberboard shall be of the following classes and styles, as specified (see 6.2 and 6.3).

Class A.—Building board (natural finish).

Class B.—Lath (for plaster base).

Class C.—Roof insulation board.

Class D.—Interior boards (factory finished).

    Style (1).—Interior-finish board.
    Style (2).—Panels (or tile board).
    Style (3).—Plank.

Class E.—Sheathing.

Class F.—Interior boards (flame-resistant-finished surface).

    Style (1).—Interior-finish board.
    Style (2).—Panels (or tile board).
    Style (3).—Plank.

Class G.—Shingle backer.

1.2.2 *Sizes and dimensions.*—Unless otherwise specified (see 6.2) the insulating fiberboard shall be furnished in commercial sizes and dimensions.

2. APPLICABLE SPECIFICATIONS, STANDARDS, AND OTHER PUBLICATIONS

2.1 Specifications and standards.—The following specifications and standards of the issues in effect on date of invitation for bids form a part of this specification to the extent specified herein.

Fed. Std. No. 123—Marking for Domestic Shipment (Civilian Agencies).

(Activities outside the Federal Government may obtain copies of Federal Specifications, Standards, and Handbooks as outlined under General Information in the Index of Federal Specifications, Standards, and Handbooks and at the prices indicated in the Index. The Index, which includes cumulative monthly supplements as issued, is for sale on a subscription basis by the Superintendent of Documents, U. S. Government Printing Office, Washington 25, D. C.

(Single copies of this specification and other product specifications required by activities outside the Federal Government for bidding purposes are available without charge at the General Services Administration Regional Offices in Boston, New York, Atlanta, Chicago, Kansas City, Mo., Dallas, Denver, San Francisco, Los Angeles, Seattle, and Washington, D. C.

(Federal Government activities may obtain copies of Federal Specifications, Standards, and Handbooks and the Index of Federal Specifications, Standards, and Handbooks from established distribution points in their agencies.)

1

570399/60/163

FSC 5640

Commercial Standard **CS35-61**

Hardwood Plywood

A recorded

voluntary standard of the

trade published by

the U.S. Department

of Commerce

For sale by the Superintendent of Documents
U.S. Government Printing Office, Washington 25, D.C.   Price 15 cents.

ASA

Reg. U. S. Pat. Off.

A42.1-1964

Revision of
A42.1-1955

UDC 693.6

American Standard Specifications for

Gypsum Plastering

Sponsors

The American Institute of Architects
American Society for Testing and Materials

Approved April 27, 1964

AMERICAN STANDARDS ASSOCIATION

INCORPORATED

AMERICAN SOCIETY FOR TESTING AND MATERIALS
1916 Race St., Philadelphia 3, Pa.

Reprinted from Copyrighted 1965 Book of ASTM Standards, Part 12.

Tentative Specification for
HOLLOW LOAD-BEARING CONCRETE MASONRY UNITS[1]

ASTM Designation: C 90 – 64 T
ISSUED, 1964.[2]

This Tentative Specification has been approved by the sponsoring committee and accepted by the Society in accordance with established procedures, for use pending adoption as standard. Suggestions for revisions should be addressed to the Society at 1916 Race St., Philadelphia 3, Pa.

Scope

1. This specification covers hollow load-bearing concrete masonry wall units made from portland cement, water and suitable mineral aggregates with or without the inclusion of other materials.

Classification

2. (*a*) *Types.*—Concrete masonry units manufactured in accordance with this specification shall conform to two types as follows:

(*1*) *Moisture-Controlled Units (Type I).*—Moisture-controlled units (type I) shall conform to all requirements of this specification including the moisture-content requirements listed in Table III. Moisture-controlled units shall be designated as Grade U-I, Grade P-I, and Grade G-I.

(*2*) *Nonmoisture-Controlled Units (Type II).* — Nonmoisture-controlled units (Type II) shall conform to all requirements of this specification except the moisture-content requirements listed in Table III. Nonmoisture-controlled units shall be designated as Grade U-II, Grade P-II, and Grade G-II.

NOTE 1.—When a particular weight class, surface texture, finish, color, uniformity of color or other special feature is desired, this feature should be specified separately by the purchaser.

(*b*) *Grades.*—Three grades of concrete masonry units in each of the two types are covered as follows (Note 1):

(*1*) *Grades U-I and U-II.*—For use in unprotected exterior walls below grade and also for unprotected exterior walls above grade which may be exposed to frost action.

(*2*) *Grades P-I and P-II.*—For use in protected exterior walls below grade and also for protected exterior walls above grade that may be exposed to frost action.

(*3*) *Grades G-I and G-II.*—For gen-

---

[1] Under the standardization procedure of the Society, this specification is under the jurisdiction of the ASTM Committee C-15 on Manufactured Masonry Units.

[2] Revised and reverted to tentative by action of the Administrative Committee on Standards, December 1, 1964.

Prior to its present publication as tentative, this specification was published as tentative rom 1931 to 1936, being revised in 1933 and 1934. It was adopted and published as standard from 1936 to 1964, being revised in 1939, 1944, 1952, and 1959.

7

SPECIFYING MATERIALS

The selection of materials and equipment in the design of a structure is the responsibility of the architect. His professional judgment dictates the quality of the item to be specified. He is likewise responsible for selecting materials for use in conjunction with other materials or assemblies of materials and equipment in a composite design. Inasmuch as he is held accountable for the success or failure of his plans and specifications, he should as a logical consequence be the master of his own fate and have ultimate control in this selection.

In many instances, standards for materials have been established by certain recognized authorities. These include ASTM Standards, Federal Specifications, USA Standards, AASHO Specifications, and Commercial Standards. These standards establish various types, grades, and qualities, and in addition may offer various options. These standards may be used if found satisfactory by the specifier, or he may upgrade their requirements by specifying additional characteristics. It is also customary and quite necessary to use trade or brand names in specifying materials when reference standards have not been developed and when, in the judgment of the architect, these brands will fulfill the project requirements.

When brand names are used as a standard in a specification, it is almost impossible to include the names of all competitive materials which the architect may be willing to use. Competition is invited in order to obtain equitable costs to the owner. To allow for the possible use of other brands or makes without naming them in endless profusion, it has been the custom to follow the names given in the specifications with the words "or equal." This device has often led to conflict between architect and contractor concerning who should determine the equality of materials proposed for substitution. Undoubtedly, no phrase in specifications has been subject to more severe criticism than the phrase "or equal." That the use of this term is not satisfactory in controlling the selection of materials and equipment specified is attested to by the problems that have arisen from its use, by the countless seminars that have been held to discuss alternative approaches, and by the many articles that have appeared over the years in attempts to arrive at a more satisfactory solution.

As a result, several other systems are in use today. Descriptions of them are set forth on the following pages, beginning with a summary of the disadvantages of the traditional "or equal" specifications.

Or Equal Specifications *Or equal* specifications usually name one, two, or several brand names and follow with the term "or equal" or "or approved equal." The following are some of the reasons which have been advanced for eliminating the term "or equal" from specifications:

1. When the "or equal" phrase is used, a bidder attempts to secure a lower price on a material than that specified, and he will be in doubt as to whether the architect will approve it. If the bidder takes a chance on this lower-price material, he risks being forced to buy the higher priced material specified. If the bidder does not take this chance, he loses the advantage of the lower price, which might make the difference between winning or losing the contract.

2. The "or equal" clause increases the amount of office work the architect must perform in order to investigate all of the "or equal" substitutions that are submitted by the contractor for approval.

3. It permits contractor more opportunity for last-minute substitutions, requiring over-hasty consideration by the architect.

4. Where a continuing project is developed in two or more phases of construction, the "or equal" clause may allow different materials to be used in the same project, and the maintenance problems of the owner are multiplied.

5. Although an alternate product may be "equal" or similar to the one specified, its use in conjunction with other assemblies, materials, or products may be unproven, unacceptable, improper, or even faulty. At times, additional costs are incurred while making adaptations to accommodate the alternate product, and such costs are difficult to resolve. While the architect derives no "benefit" in making adaptations, it often has caused additional expense to the architect in connection with the changes.

6. It contributes heavily to "bid shopping," which results in delays in construction, since the substitution is usually submitted at the last moment and interferes with the routine process of careful evaluation by the architect.

7. It takes control of the project away from the architect who is responsible for its execution.

Open Specifications The open specification for materials and equipment is written without reference to brand names or proprietary makes. This type of specification is used most commonly for public work, and may be used in private work. It can be written quite simply by the use of "reference specifications" which make reference to recognized standards discussed in Chapter 6. In the absence of standards for some items, notably for mechanical and electrical equipment, a descriptive specification must be prepared to present complete and comprehensive data on the product required. The open specification is intended to invite the greatest amount of competition and to maintain complete impartiality between various manufacturers.

The open specification can be used for many basic materials when reference is made to recognized standards. These standards include such materials as structural steel, cement, gypsum plaster, ceramic tile, concrete masonry units, roofing felts and bitumen, and a host of other materials. It becomes inadequate when the architect seeks to specify paints, many sealants, concrete admixtures, elastomeric waterproofing materials, and, generally, the man-made products of chemistry, since the promulgation of adequate standards lags far behind the development of these products. Standards are likewise inadequate for specifying such equipment as boilers, lighting fixtures, fans, pumps, and other items of a mechanical or electrical nature. For these products, the architect and engineer contrive to write an open specification setting forth descriptive or performance characteristics which create voluminous specifications.

When reference specifications are used, the architect and engineer can approve submissions quite readily by requiring certifications from manufacturers attesting to compliance of their products with the standards specified. However, when descriptive or performance specifications for materials and equipment are employed, the architect and engineer must carefully check the submission against all of the provisions which have been minutely specified. Failure to check against compliance with even one aspect of his own specifications, which may result in a subsequent failure, can lead to legal action against him by the owner for having approved a product which did not comply with the specifications.

A base bid or closed specification is one in which the architect specifies only one brand name or proprietary make for each individual material, piece of equipment, or product. Occasionally he may augment this brand name with a brief descriptive specification or cite certain performance characteristics. The intent of this type of specification is to limit the bidding to products

Base Bid, or Closed Specifications

which the architect or engineer has specifically selected for the project. The bidder has no choice under this base bid specification.

Under this system, product selection and responsibility rests entirely with the architect. It enables the architect to set room sizes, headroom, and vital dimensions, since no substitutes are permitted which may affect dimensions, clearances, and foundations, especially for mechanical equipment. In addition, bid shopping is eliminated, which does away with the unnecessary construction delays which are a by-product of this practice.

Under this system, competition is excluded, and the owner does not necessarily get the best value for his dollar. The architect is sometimes unfairly accused of favoritism by the manufacturer or supplier not included in the specifications. The contractor is compelled to use the product of a manufacturer or a supplier with whom he does not regularly do business and may experience difficulty with credit and delivery. In addition, the contractor may not have had experience in the installation of the specific product named and may be required to guarantee an installation with which he has had no previous experience.

Bidders Choice or Restricted Specifications

The "bidders choice" or "restricted specification" is akin to the base bid or closed specification, except that the architect names two or more brand names or proprietary makes for each item he wishes to use.

The architect should investigate each of the products he proposes to specify, to make certain that like or equal products are put into competition with one another. It has an advantage over the base bid specification, in that competition is invited. The architect must be careful not to equate several materials where one is so much lower in price that it negates the advantage of competitive bidding and, in effect, creates a closed specification.

Bidders List of Substitutions

Under this method, the bidder is permitted to submit alternates or substitutions from the materials or equipment specified. These substitutions are listed and included with his bid, along with the net difference in cost if the substitution is accepted. Generally, the bid must also include the name, brand, catalog number, and manufacturer of the proposed substitute, together with complete specifications and descriptive data.

When one calculates the hundreds of items used in the construction of a building and the quantity of products manufactured, the number of substitutions can be staggering. An evaluation and analysis of bids to determine an acceptable low bidder would be a Herculean task, and the bids would no longer be predicated on the architect's original selection of materials and equipment.

This method does not entirely achieve the element of competition. Since each bidder is free to submit any substitution, and since each of the bidders is unaware of what substitutions his competitor may offer, there is no competition on the substitutions offered.

Product Approval Standards

Under this method, products are clearly defined by using specification standards where possible, by using specific product names, by specifying more than one product where possible, and by listing basic criteria where desirable. Bids are based on the use of any product meeting established standards (such as ASTM) or the products specified. However, upon application, bidders are permitted to request approval of products during the bidding period, within established limits. If the architect does approve the product, it is listed in an addendum so that all bidders compete on the same basis.

It is recognized that some of the disadvantages of methods previously discussed can be applied to this method. However, this method *does* achieve the following:
a. Control of products by the architect.
b. Competition.
c. Fairness in attracting other products of which the architect may not have been aware at the time of preparation of documents.
d. Elimination of the risk to bidders in accepting products other than those specified.
e. Closer bidding.
f. Discouragement of bid peddling, or shopping.
g. Administration of equality at the proper time and by the proper agency.
h. Complete flexibility.

Under this method manufacturers of materials and equipment receive consideration under competitive bidding procedures. The auction is over when the bids are submitted. The possibility of the successful contractor submitting after award of a contract (under the "or equal" method), material or equipment not previously known to all bidders, and which in effect prevents the owner from obtaining competitive prices, is precluded.

This method lends itself to use in projects involving public funds. According to the United States General Accounting Office, this procedure may be used by federal agencies if they so decide. Legal officers in state, county, and municipal governments may likewise be apprised of this solution and may give approval to this method so that the use of the term "or equal" as it has been used and abused, is placed in proper perspective.

It should be noted that the intent of equality to obtain competition is not changed or excluded from the specification, but rather the time for evaluation is adjusted so as to occur prior to the bid date.

The greatest apparent drawback is the possibility of a substantial number of requests for approval, within a limited time. Carefully prepared specifications, a slightly extended bidding period, and allotment of sufficient time prior to bid date as the deadline for approvals, minimizes the problem.

Control of the project is achieved, so that at the time bids are received there is no doubt about the quality of products to be used. Competition is obtained through the basic qualification. In addition, other products that prove to be acceptable can further increase competition. No one with an acceptable product need be kept out. Prime contract bidders can be confident of the product bids they are using in their estimates. Less gamble, less contingency, and sharper bidding are the results.

Bid peddling and shopping are reduced, resulting in more competitive bids from product suppliers. The competitive products are known, and it is also known that a lower priced nonspecified product cannot be offered, and possibly accepted, after bids are received. Therefore, the best price possible consistent with the desired quality can be offered as a firm bid, with reasonable assurance that the price will not be undercut by an unknown or "non-equal." This method removes the problem of bidders claiming that a certain product is "equal," and that it was used in their bid. The contractor is not damaged financially as a result of a rejected product. Complete flexibility can be easily realized. Recognized standards can be used completely if available. One product or twenty can be specified, depending on criteria and the owner's requirements, and every element of design and function can be considered. Conditions can be varied from project to project, and from public work to private work. The length of time for approvals can be varied.

The same care is essential with this method as it is with most others. Products must be properly and clearly specified. The basis for evaluation of products must be stated. Proposed substitutions must be given complete consideration, careful review, and honest evaluation.

State or specify the conditions only *once*—under the appropriate article of the general or supplemental conditions; this establishes the conditions of consideration. The term "or equal" is omitted under individual specification sections or detailed requirements. This forces a bidder to refer to the proper article regarding approval. List all known products acceptable for the project. This is not an overwhelming task; a file can soon be built up to reduce the bulk of the work for most items. Wherever possible, use only those established standards—such as ASTM, Federal Specifications, and the like—which have been determined acceptable for the project, modifying them where necessary. Insofar as possible, list basic criteria that must be met for product consideration. However, meeting this criteria may not always qualify a product, because of intangibles and variables.

Administration of Product Approval Standards

Written requests are essential, and should be mandatory for these reasons:
1. They form a basis of understanding in the event of a later claim of misinterpretation.
2. Endless worthless hours on the telephone with persons who are reasonably sure that their product does not comply, but who feel that a phone try is worthwhile, are eliminated.
3. Written requests are generally submitted only by persons with a genuine interest in bidding.
4. They permit a review and evaluation in the quiet of normal office procedure, without the pressure of a sales pitch.
5. For a given level of quality, they weed out requests for products that are obviously below requirements. After an unsuccessful attempt or two, the person making the request stops trying.

Requests should be considered only from prime bidders. Time must be allotted for review and evaluation of requests. This may be difficult at first. However, time always has to be made available for such a review after bids are received, and the process is merely reversed to pre-bid time. This method must be administered and enforced with a strong will. Deviations cannot be permitted (even to "friends" in the industry). If the product is not specified, it cannot be used.

Occasionally an "equal" product is omitted, possibly by oversight. This does not change the conditions, and if the manufacturer does not find his product in the specification he should request that it be included by one of the prime bidders. Each job and each owner's prejudices are individual considerations. A manufacturer cannot *assume* that he is approved.

In fairness to bidders, prompt consideration should be given. Addenda should be issued as the bidding period progresses, in order that those who make early application may know whether they are approved or not, in time for their "take off."

Specifying Product Approval Standards The following language should be incorporated in the Supplementary Conditions if product approval standards are to be used as the method for specifying materials:

1. Wherever the word "product" appears herein it shall mean material, equipment, assembly, manufacturers, brands, trade name, items or similar description as applicable.
2. The intent of this article is to encourage and permit competition on qualified products by all reputable and qualified contractors, suppliers, and manufacturers whose products, reputations, and performances warrant approval for the conditions, intent of design, and performance considerations.
3. Whenever any product is specified in accordance with a Federal Specification, an ASTM Standard, and United States Standard Specification, or other association standard, the Contractor shall present an affidavit from the manufacturer certifying that the product complies with the particular standard specification. Where necessary and requested or specified, support test data shall be submitted to substantiate compliance.
4. Whenever any product is specified or shown by describing proprietary items, model numbers, catalog numbers, manufacturer, trade names, or similar reference, the bidder obligates himself to submit proposals and accept awards of contracts based upon the use of such products. Use of such reference is intended to establish the measure of quality which the Architect has determined as requisite and necessary for the project. Where two or more products are shown or specified, the bidder has his option of which to use, provided the

product used meets all requirements of specifications and design criteria. The right is reserved to approve or disapprove proposed deviations in design, function, construction, or similar differences that will affect the design intent.

5. For approval of products other than those specified, bidders shall submit a request in writing at least ____ days (note: seven days recommended as a minimum) prior to bid date and hour. Requests received after this time will not be reviewed or considered regardless of cause. Requests shall clearly define and described the product for which approval is requested. Requests shall be accompanied by manufacturer's literature, specifications, drawings, cuts, performance data, list of references, or other information necessary to completely describe the item. Approval by the Architect will be in the form of an addendum to the specifications issued to all prospective prime contract bidders on record. The addendum will indicate the additional products which are approved for this project.

6. Substitution or approval of products will be considered after bids are opened only under the following conditions:

a. The Contractor shall place orders for specified materials and equipment promptly upon award of contract. No excuse or proposed substitution will be considered for materials and equipment due to unavailability unless proof is submitted that firm orders were placed 10 days after approval by the Architect of the item listed in the specifications.

b. The reason for the unavailability is beyond the control of the Contractor. Unavailability will be construed as being due to strikes, bankruptcy, discontinuance of the manufacture of a product, or Acts of God.

c. Requests for such substitution shall be made in writing to the Architect after the award of a contract and within ten days of the date on which the Contractor ascertains that he cannot obtain the material or equipment specified.

d. Requests shall be accompanied by a complete description of the material or equipment which the Contractor wishes to use as a substitute.

e. Substitutions must be approved by the Architect in writing.

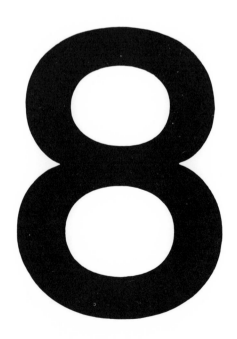

SPECIFICATION WRITING

TECHNIQUES

General

Specification writing techniques embody certain methods of presentation of information and instructions peculiar to this literary form, and are therefore different from an essay or a novel. The specifications are written instructions intended to complement the graphic illustrations on the drawings. Since both documents are combined to convey the entire message, the information contained in the specifications should be presented in a form that interlocks and does not overlap.

Scope of Work

A common form of duplication in specification writing which is superfluous and which may be dangerous is the use of a heading entitled "Scope of Work," or "Work Included," under which the work specified in detail in the ensuing section is summarized in outline form under this heading. Many specification writers may disagree with this assertion, and I cannot hope to make any converts out of this group. However, a review of the fundamentals of specification writing will convince the specifications trainee that the Scope of Work subhead, as written by some practitioners, is redundant, dangerous, time-consuming, and simply amounts to padding of the specifications.

The danger in preparing a Scope of Work lies in duplication. The difficulties created by duplication are elaborated upon under the heading *Duplication-Repetition* in this Chapter. For example, there have been specifications with a Scope of Work written for masonry which goes into such detail as follows:

The work under this contract shall include all labor and materials required for the construction of the masonry work as follows:
   a. Exterior face brick in cavity-wall construction with concrete-block back-up.
   b. Exterior face brick with stone-concrete back-up.
   c. Exterior face brick with common-brick back-up for parapets.
   d. Common brick for interior partitions where noted.
   e. Concrete block for back-up in exterior masonry walls.
   f. Concrete block for interior partitions where noted.
   g. Structural facing-tile soaps at exterior walls.

This is not quite the end of the Scope of Work, as it goes on *ad infinitum, ad nauseum.* What has the specification writer accomplished? Has he given the estimator information to price the work, the builder's superintendent directions in construction, or the architect's supervisor a check on the character and quality of materials and workmanship?

The drawings, if properly drawn, will indicate the location of all of the materials. The specifications should not and need not describe their location, since the draftsman may make subsequent changes without notifying the specifications writer. Another danger that sometimes results is that this Scope of Work list is not expanded upon later in the specification, leaving only a brief outline in the Scope of Work which is incomplete and forms no sound basis for bidding. The estimator cannot use the Scope of Work as complete, for fear that he will not make a comprehensive take-off. The danger with the Scope of Work paragraphs is that they are not complete but only indicate the major portions of the work under the section. The estimator may accept the Scope of Work as complete and fail to read the remainder of the specifications, which contain other information essential for an accurate estimate.

While there may be some items listed in the Scope of Work which are not completely described in the specifications, there are also items of work sometimes described in the specifications but not listed in the scope. A contractor may contend that he should not be required to furnish anything not listed in the Scope of Work. Lawsuits have been started on lesser grounds, but this is not the only problem. It is the incident trouble and annoyance to the owner and the possible delay to the job that must be avoided. The argument in favor of the Scope of Work clauses is that they are a convenience to the contractor, but such clauses tend to lead the estimator pressed for time into the too-common error of accepting the Scope of Work as sufficient in itself—with disastrous results.

Article 4.4.1 of the "AIA General Conditions" states that the contractor shall include all labor and materials necessary for the proper execution of the work. The General Conditions, in turn, are a part of the contract documents, and when the technical sections are written specifying clearly all materials and labor and everything necessary to secure the construction of all that part of the building properly included in that technical section, a Scope of Work becomes redundant.

In general, the section title should be indicative of the scope of the section, and the table of contents is useful in alerting a contractor to any subdivision of similar work. For example, the section "Concrete Work" by itself in the table of contents would indicate that this section included all concrete work; whereas a table of contents that included such sections as "Concrete

Roads and Walks," "Concrete Work," and "Precast Architectural Concrete" would inform the contractor that there is a subdivision of these items of concrete. Similarly, if the table of contents listed only "Unit Masonry," then all masonry work would be included under this heading; whereas a table of contents listing "Brickwork," "Structural Facing Tile," and "Gypsum Blockwork" would alert the contractor to a breakdown of masonry work shown on the drawings as being specified under separate section titles.

There are instances however, where a section title may not necessarily be completely informative, and a delineation of the work included under the section may be required. For example, the section title "Curtain Wall" may be used in one specification, but its content may include glazing, sealing, venetian blind pockets, and convector enclosures. In another specification the section title "Curtain Wall" may be limited to only the metal framing and metal panels, with the glazing, sealing, and other items specified under their respective sections. In this instance, a comprehensive Scope of Work would be appropriate to define the content of the section entitled "Curtain Wall."

If it is necessary to provide the contractor with an itemized list of the subjects contained in the specifications, it may be furnished in the form of a complete table of contents. This is quite evidently a convenience only, and an omission cannot do the legal harm that might be caused by an incomplete statement of work included under the Scope of Work.

In effect, when the specification writer utilizes a section title for a Scope of Work, or if he writes an abbreviated Scope of Work as follows,

> The work under this section of the specifications includes all labor, materials, equipment and services necessary to complete the concrete work as shown on the drawings and herein specified

he has specified *all* concrete work under this one section. There is then no reason for him to enumerate concrete foundations, pits, walls, slabs, beams, and girders. It should be obvious that if the drawing indicates an item to be concrete, a specification for concrete materials and the placing of same has included all concrete shown. This simplified scope and the heading "Work of Other Sections" described below, should be sufficient to define what is and what is not the work covered by a specific technical section.

Work of Other Sections The heading Work of Other Sections should be reserved to exclude from a section those items a contractor might normally expect to find under a specific section, but which the specification writer for good and sufficient reasons has elected to specify under another section. For example, under the earthwork section the heading Work of Other Sections could list the following:

1. Excavation, trenching, and backfilling for mechanical and electrical work is specified under their respective sections.
2. Furnishing of topsoil is specified under "Lawn and Planting."

Under the concrete section the heading Work of Other Sections could list the following:

1. Concrete bases for mechanical and electrical equipment is specified under their respective sections.

By utilizing the section title "Concrete Work" as a scope of work, or by writing an abbreviated scope of work in the manner previously illustrated, the specification writer in effect is stating that all concrete work is specified in this section, and that the only exceptions are the concrete bases for mechanical and electrical equipment, which are listed under Work of Other Sections as being specified elsewhere. It is far simpler and safer to exclude an item by the device of the Work of Other Sections than to attempt to enumerate under a Scope of Work the sum of the parts that make up the whole.

Unfortunately, there are some specifications that use headings such as "work by others" and "work not included" as a substitute for Work of Other Sections. These headings can be misleading, inasmuch as they imply that the work listed under these headings are not part of the contract. The heading "work not included" should be reserved for, and used only for, listing those items that are not to be included as part of a contract.

The heading Work of Other Sections should not list related items not pertinent to the scope of a particular section. For example, under the heading Work of Other Sections in a built-up roofing section, the following has been listed:

"Work of Other Sections"
1. Membrane Waterproofing
2. Dampproofing

Any subcontractor will understand that work in no way related to his own is naturally not included, especially if it is not mentioned in the section. It is only work that reasonably might be inferred to be part of this work that should be listed as specified under the work of another section when that is the architect's intention.

A heading "work not included," if properly used, should not be encumbered with work that is not normally done, which can be illustrated by a typical paragraph found in a painting section as follows:

"Work Not Included"
1. Painting of asphalt tile
2. Painting of glass
3. Painting marble

Certainly, if the specification writer describes paint materials and their application on specific surfaces—such as wood, ferrous metal, plaster and concrete block—the contractor will not paint asphalt tile, glass, and marble, whether listed under the "work not included" heading or not.

Individuals not properly grounded in the principles of specification writing habitually fall back on general and all-inclusive language which often results in what are termed "grandfather clauses" by specification writers and "murder clauses" by contractors—clauses which embrace everything, yet fail to be specific. A typical example of a grandfather clause might read as follows: "the contractor shall furnish and include everything necessary for the full and complete construction of the building whether shown or specified or not shown or described." When an architect is incompetent, he will entrench himself behind such a series of clauses, which may be interpreted to mean anything or nothing. In their failure to be specific, these clauses will, during the course of construction, require interpretations by the architect which may be difficult to enforce.

Grandfather Clauses

A clause such as "concrete floors shall be finished level as approved by the architect," without stating a tolerance, means to the contractor, "Guess what I will make you do!" An instruction to a contractor by means of a drawing or a specification must be specific, and no architect should expect a contractor to fulfill a non-specific requirement.

Where several different kinds or classes of similar materials are used, they should be described in a manner that permits some material to be specified for every part of the building. Such a technique has been borrowed from the legal profession and is a system known as the residuary legatee.

Residuary Legatee

67

To illustrate, let us assume that in preparing a will, an individual wishes to leave the bulk of his estate to his wife, but wishes to make several minor bequests to his children or to relatives. He first enumerates his minor bequests and then states, in substance, "the residue of my property I bequeath to my wife." She is then known as the "residuary legatee."

In applying this principle to specification writing, the materials occurring in the smallest quantity or in the fewest places should be listed first, the material occurring in the remaining places becomes the "residuary legatee" and can be covered by some such phrase as "the rest of the building."

As example of this technique the following samples are offered:
1. In specifying glass one can enumerate the following:
    a. Obscure glass—all toilet rooms
    b. Tempered glass—entrance doors and side lights
    c. Plate glass—borrowed lights
    d. Window glass—all other locations
2. In specifying paint:
    a. Plaster surfaces in toilets—semi-gloss enamel
    b. All other plaster—latex emulsion paint
3. In specifying concrete:
    a. 2500 psi concrete—concrete foundations
    b. 3000 psi concrete—concrete pavements
    c. 3500 psi concrete—all other concrete work

If this method is followed, some material will always be specified for every part of the building, while any other plan obliges the specification writer to check all his listings most carefully, for fear of not having included some minor portion.

Duplication—Repetition In Chapter 2 it has been noted that the necessary information for the construction of a building is communicated to a contractor in two forms, graphic (the drawings) and written (the specifications), and that these documents should complement one another. If this information overlaps, there can be duplication which may lead to a difference in instructions and disagreement as to which is the proper document to follow.

If this duplication were exact in each instance and remained so, it might be harmless at best; but too often, the information presented on the drawings and that specified either does not agree in the first place, or, owing to last minute changes, errors and differences develop which create entirely new meanings. Repetition in the contract documents is always dangerous and should be avoided.

Technically, duplication is an exact repetition, word for word, of a sentence or a paragraph in a specification, or else it is an exact repetition of a detail on a drawing. For example, a steel ladder might be detailed on a drawing, giving the size of the side members and the diameter and the spacing of the rungs. The specification should describe the quality of the material and how the rungs are let into the side members, but it should not repeat the sizes and spacing, since the drawing may be altered by the draftsman, with a resulting conflict in the two documents. The unnecessary expense involved in writing and reproducing statements which merely repeat may be minor in comparison to the ultimate cost to the owner of mistakes in specification interpretation.

An exact duplication in the specification or drawing should cause no misunderstanding. However, it is seldom that we see an exact duplication. In most cases the specification writer will attempt to avoid duplication or repetition by stating in different words what has been said or stated elsewhere, in order to amplify. But it is precisely in attempting to amplify or reiterate in different words that conflict and ambiguity occur. It is therefore good practice to make a statement only once; if it is not satisfactory, it should be discarded and re-written, rather than amplified or explained in other terms.

9

SPECIFICATION LANGUAGE

It is not intended, nor indeed is it possible, for this chapter to be a treatise on English grammar and readable writing. Rather, it is proposed that we direct ourselves to the reasons why it is necessary to use proper specification language. Each statement in a specification, whether it is concerned with specifying materials, instructing a contractor with installation procedures, or describing workmanship, carries a dollar sign alongside it. The contractor expects to be paid for each order given him by the specification writer, and the contractor's bid reflects every statement in the specifications. Using vague, ambiguous language indicates that the specification writer may want something but is unsure about demanding it. Statements such as "tests will be required unless waived," "additional shop drawings and samples may be required," and "uneven surfaces may be cause for rejection" are examples of equivocation that plague the contractor. Specification language should be precise, not vague. The precise specification can be enforced; the vague one may be difficult to enforce and will still cost the owner money, because the contractor has included the cost in his bid.

The essential requirement in writing specifications, aside from technical know-how, is the ability to express one's self in good English. Although the specifications are one of the contract documents that becomes a legal document, legal phraseology is not necessary. A statement in good, clear English may be even more definite, unequivocal, and understandable to the superintendent and the foreman than legal wording.

Language is a means of communication. Unlike graphic communication, where symbols and crosshatching have precise meanings, words must be carefully selected to transmit information. There are subtle variations in the choice of language, and the word or term selected to communicate an instruction may be interpreted by a contractor quite differently from that which was intended by the specification writer.

Consider the word *smooth*. The dictionary defines it as "having an even surface; devoid of surface roughness." The term "smooth" has been employed in specifications as follows: "Bituminous road surfaces shall be smooth," yet a preferred texture for the surface to reduce skidding is a rough texture. Concrete floors have been specified to have a smooth, wood float finish; or a smooth, rubbed finish; or a smooth trowelled finish. However, in each case the degree of smoothness varies. It would be preferable to select the tool which will accomplish a result and rely upon it to achieve the surface finish desired by specifying its use as follows: "Concrete floors shall be finished with a wood trowel," or "concrete steps shall be rubbed with carborundum stone," or "concrete floors shall be steel trowelled."

In order to communicate by language, the architect should visualize grammar as well as he perceives design. Grammar is not just obeying rules, it is the power politics of language. Words rule other words, subjects have objects. Prepositions are powerful indicators, instruments of authority, traffic directors. All this suggests the visual, and grammar should be visualized as much as possible.

There are three important *C*'s for specification writing. The wording of specifications should be Clear, Correct and Concise: clear so there is no ambiguity; correct technically; and concise so there is no excessive verbiage. A good specification is one containing the fewest words that can be used to complete the description and make sense. Verbosity and repetition lead to ambiguity.

Considering those who are to use the specifications, it is evident that specifications must be made clear to some whose vocabulary may be limited. The meaning should be grasped readily even by the workmen. A specification written in English that is clear even to the mechanics on the job is the logical form to use. If a mechanic cannot interpret specifications, he will not be able to execute them.

Since specifications are instructions to the contractor, they should be definite and mandatory. To be mandatory they must be imperative. Therefore use the imperative "shall" with reference to the work of the contractor and never the vague and indefinite "will" or "to be." The proper place to use "will" is in a statement describing the acts of the owner or the architect.

Superior examples of specification language are contained in a textbook entitled *Specifications,* by H. Griffith Edwards, FAIA, FCSI, copyright 1961, D. Van Nostrand Co., Inc., Princeton, N.J., a portion of which is reproduced here with the permission of the author and the publisher.

CHAPTER 6

Specification Language

6–1 GENERAL

The specification writer should present his instructions regarding construction work to be undertaken in such a manner that the drawings are more clearly interpreted and everyone's responsibility is designated without question. Specifications are read by contractors, construction superintendents, foremen and others connected with the building trades who should not be required to interpret subtle shades of meaning or stilted terms. The writer should use trade terms and clear language written in a simple manner. The aim of this chapter is to give a few pointers on how to achieve such a style.

6–2 PHRASEOLOGY

In the development of early specifications stiffly formal terms and sentences were borrowed and have been recopied (many times without thought) throughout the years. Old-fashioned legal phraseology should be avoided in specifications, and clear technical language should be used instead.

6–3 STREAMLINED SPECIFICATIONS

a. A specification should be judged by its quality and not its length. The writer should always make an effort to reduce the verbiage used to describe methods and materials. This can be accomplished in many ways; several are suggested in this book.

b. One authority proposes writing specifications in outline form without the use of complete sentences (see *Streamlined Specifications* by H. W. Peaselee, F.A.I.A., *Pencil Points,* August 1939). The outline form serves very well for materials, but it is difficult to adapt it to the description of methods, and therefore the author recommends the use of complete sentences throughout the specifications or at least for those portions where methods are described.

6–4 SENTENCES

Sentences should be crisp, concise and short, written with simple words. If a sentence becomes too long and involved, it should be rewritten and made into two or more short sentences. It is more important to present facts clearly than it is to develop an elegant style of writing.

6–5 PUNCTUATION

All sentences and clauses should be written carefully to permit punctuation marks to be added, eliminated or misplaced without changing the meaning. Use as few punctuation marks as possible, particularly commas.

6–6 CAPITALIZATION

In specification writing follow the general rules regarding use of capitals for the first letter in words, and in addition capitalize the following:

1. Parties to the contract, including *Owner, Contractor* and *Architect.*
2. Spaces of the building, such as *Bed Room, Living Room* and *Office.*
3. The Contract documents, such as *Working Drawings, Specifications, General Conditions* and *Agreement* or *Contract.*
4. Grades of materials, such as *B and Better Southern Pine* and *Intermediate Heat Duty Fire Clay Brick.*

The use of capitals in these instances serves to clarify references in the body of the text.

6–7 TENSE

a. Although some authorities recommend the use of the same verb tense throughout a set of specifications, this may cause unnecessary wordiness and monotony.

b. *Simple Imperative Mood:* The simple imperative mood may be substituted for the emphatic future tense to advantage, effecting an economy of words. For example:

> "Contractor shall install lighting fixtures which will be furnished by Owner."

can be written:

> "Install lighting fixtures which will be furnished by Owner."

c. *Simple Present Infinitive,* likewise, may be substituted for the simple future tense; for example, the phrase above:

> "Install lighting fixtures which will be furnished by Owner."

can be written:

> "Install lighting fixtures to be furnished by Owner."

6–8 PRONOUNS

Minimize the use of pronouns. It is better to repeat the noun than risk possible misunderstanding.

6–9 WORDS AND PHRASES

a. Following is a list of words and phrases frequently misused in specification writing and should be particularly noted:

b. *Shall:*   Use *shall* in connection with acts of the Contractor, or with labor, materials and equipment to be furnished by him.

                  Poor: "Contractor will install finish hardware."

                                    "Footings will rest on undisturbed soil."

                  Better: "Contractor shall install finish hardware."

                                      "Footings shall rest on undisturbed soil."

c. *Will:*   Use *will* in connection with acts of the Owner or Architect.

                  Poor: "Lighting fixtures shall be furnished by Owner."

                  Better: "Lighting fixtures will be furnished by Owner."

d. *Must:*   Avoid the use of *must* and *is to* and substitute the word *shall* to prevent the inference of different degrees of obligation.

e. *Any:*   For the reason that *any* implies a choice, it should not be used when a choice is not intended, as for example:

                  Poor: "Any materials condemned or rejected shall be removed."

                  Better: "Materials condemned or rejected shall be removed."

f. *Either:*   The word *both* should be substituted for *either* when no choice is intended.

                  Poor: "Glass panels shall be installed on either side of main entrance."

                  Better: "Glass panels shall be installed on both sides of main entrance."

g. *Of:*   The preposition *of* often may be eliminated to shorten the text.

                  Poor: "For colors see Schedule of Paint Finishes."

                  Better: "For colors see Paint Finish Schedule."

                  Poor: "Apply one coat of stipple finish to walls in the Office of the Manager."

                  Better: "Apply one stipple finish coat to walls in Manager's Office."

h. *The:*   Definite article *the* and indefinite articles *a* and *an* need not be used in many instances.

                  Poor: "Apply an oil paint with a brush to the walls."

                  Better: "Apply oil paint with brush to walls."

i. All: The use of the word *all* is frequently unnecessary.

                       Poor: "Store all millwork under shelter."

                       Better: "Store millwork under shelter."

j. Which: *Which* and other relative pronouns should be used sparingly, if at all.

                       Poor: "Contractor shall install bathroom accessories which are to be purchased under an allowance."

                       Better: "Contractor shall install bathroom accessories to be purchased under an allowance."

k. Same: Do not use *same* as a pronoun.

                       Poor: "If materials are rejected, the Contractor shall replace same at no additional cost."

                       Better: "Contractor shall replace rejected materials at no additional cost."

l. Said: Do not use *said* as an adjective.

                       Poor: "Said materials shall be replaced at no additional cost."

                       Better: "Rejected materials shall be replaced at no additional cost."

m. And/or.   This is a stilted legal expression. The word *or* or *both* should be used in place of *and/or*.

                       Poor: "Brick shall be made of clay and/or shale."

                                     "Defects of workmanship and/or materials . . ."

                       Better: "Brick shall be made of clay, shale or a combination of both."

                                       "Defects of workmanship or materials . . ."

n. Etc.:   Placed at the end of a list of items, *etc.* shows that the specification writer obviously does not know of what the complete list consists, or he is too lazy to write it out. The use of *etc.* is vague, throws unnecessary responsibility upon the Contractor, and therefore should not be used. As one specification writer puts it, "It is better to be definite even if you are wrong; then, at least, there is a firm basis for negotiating the corrections."

o. Contractor Shall
*   Furnish and Install:*   Since it is established by Article 3 of the A.I.A. Short Form of Contract recommended, there is no need for repeating in other sections the phrase, "Contractor shall furnish and install. . . ."

p. To the Satisfaction
*   of the Architect:*   "To the satisfaction of the Architect," "As the

Architect may direct," "Acceptable to the Architect," "In the opinion of the Architect," and similar phrases should be avoided. Instead, specify exactly what the Architect's directions are, or definitely what would be satisfactory or acceptable to him. Do not leave Contractor guessing and at the mercy of Architect's future decisions.

q. *Or Equal:* *Or Equal, equal to, other approved equal, just as good* or similar expressions too often seen in specifications should not be used since the Contractor has no way of knowing what the Architect would consider equal to the brand specified. The architect might not agree with the Contractor's opinion of an *equal* product. Alternative is to specify two or more brands and allow Contractor the option of using any one.

> *Poor:* "Insulating glass shall be equal to 'Thermopane' as manufactured by Libbey-Owens-Ford Glass Company."
>
> *Better:* "Insulating glass shall be 'Thermopane' as manufactured by the Libbey-Owens-Ford Glass Company or 'Twindow' as manufactured by the Pittsburgh Plate Glass Company."

r. *A Workmanlike Job:* "A workmanlike job," "a high-class job," "a first-class job," and similar phrases should not be employed; type of workmanship expected should be described in detail.

s. *Numerals:* The practice of using numerals, rather than writing out the numbers throughout specifications, is recommended for the reason that numerals are used on the drawings and they make for clearer, easier reading. Numerals on the drawings, which are part of the contract documents, are considered legally binding and numerals in specifications are likewise legally binding.

> *Poor:* "Four feet, six inches," "Twenty-six gauge"
>
> *Better:* "4' 6"," "26 gauge"

t. *Contractor:* It is considered better practice in specification writing not to use *Contractor* as the subject of a sentence. Instead make the *material* or the *method* the subject.

> *Poor:* "Contractor shall lay brick in common bond."
>
> *Better:* "Brick shall be laid in common bond."

u. *Mechanical Contractor:* *The Mechanical Contractor, The Plumbing Contractor, The Heating Contractor, The Electrical Con-*

tractor, The General Contractor, and similar designations should be avoided. Instead the specifications should be written as if all the work is to be done by one construction firm. Of course, the Contractor always sublets some of the work and a great effort should be made to separate properly the requirements under appropriate trade sections to facilitate this. To name who is to do what robs the Contractor of his prerogative of distributing the work among Subcontractors as he sees fit.

v. *Comply with:*

When reference is made in a specification to a standard, it is better to state that the material *shall meet the requirements of* or *shall be in accordance with* than it *shall comply with* the standard.

Poor: "Structural steel shall comply with ASTM Spec. A7."

Better: "Structural steel shall meet the requirements of ASTM Spec. A7."

6–10 SIMPLIFIED SPELLING

Simplified spelling appears in some specifications, consisting mainly of: *Gage* for *Gauge; Molding* for *Moulding; Calk* for *Caulk;* and *Thru* for *Through;* a specification writer should select the spelling he prefers and be consistent.

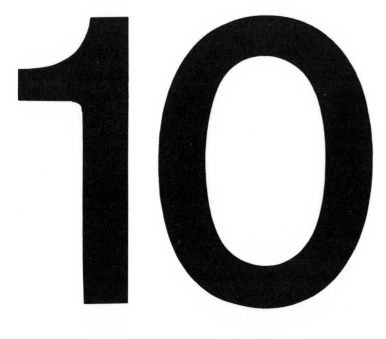

10

BIDDING REQUIREMENTS

Bidding requirements consist of those documents which are **General** used in the solicitation of bids by an owner or an agency, and are directed to bidders who might be interested in submitting bids for a project. These documents consist of three essential forms dealing with advertising, or notifying interested bidders of the existence of a proposed project; instructions pertaining to the submission of a proposal or bid; and the sample form on which the bid is to be executed by a bidder.

The three documents are as follows:

> Invitation to Bid
> Instructions to Bidders
> Bid Form

Because of the varying practices of individual specification writers and the lack of order and terminology of the material preceding the technical specifications, some chaos and non-uniformity in the arrangement and nomenclature of these documents has existed.

Bidding requirements are not "specifications." The basic difference lies in the fact that the former apply to a bidder prior to making an award, while the latter apply to a contractor and his obligations after an award is made. Generally speaking, certain information contained in the bidding requirements which is pertinent to a contractor's obligations—such as time for completion, liquidated damages, base bid, alternates, and unit prices—should be entered into the agreement or contract form to insure its fulfillment by the contractor.

Invitations to bid are generally circulated in the case of private work to certain selected bidders, and in the case of public agencies they are advertised in local newspapers. In any event, the invitation to bid, along with the instructions to bidders and a sample copy of the bid form, should be bound in the specifications.

Other terms have been used, and are used somewhat incor- **Invitation to Bid** rectly as the heading for this document. These include Advertisement to Bid (sometimes used in public work for public advertising), Notice to Bidders, and Notification to Contractors. The term "Invitation to Bid" is preferred since it best describes the intent of this document. The purposes of an "Invitation to Bid" are to attract bidders in sufficient numbers to ensure fair competition, and to notify all parties who might be interested in

81

submitting proposals. It should be limited to information which will tell a prospective bidder whether the work is in his line, whether it is within his capacity, and whether he will have the time to prepare a bid prior to opening. It should be brief and simple, and free from extraneous and irrelevant subject matter not consistent with its purpose. It should consist of these essential elements:

1. Project Title: State the name of the project, its location, and project number if any.
2. Identification of Principals: State the name and address of the architect or issuing agency, together with the date of issue.
3. Time and Place for Receipt of Bids: State the time and place where bids will be received and whether they will be publicly opened. If opened privately, indicate whether prime bidders may attend.
4. Project Description: Provide a brief but adequate description of the project, setting forth size and height and any unusual features, so that the bidder will be in a position to determine whether he has the financial and technical ability to undertake the construction of the project.
5. Type of Contract: State whether bids are being solicited for a single or a segregated contract and on what basis.
6. Examination and Procurement of Documents: State where the contract documents may be examined and when and where they may be obtained. Indicate whether a deposit or a charge will be required for procurement of the documents and whether there will be any refunds.
7. Bid Security: State whether a bid bond or other type of bid guarantee will be required to insure the execution of the contract.
8. Guaranty Bonds: State whether Performance Bonds and Labor and Materials Payment Bonds will be required to insure the completion of the contract.

Instructions to Bidders The Instructions to Bidders have also been identified by other terms, such as Information for Bidders and Conditions of Bid. The purpose of the Instructions to Bidders is to outline the requirements necessary to properly prepare and submit a bid. As such, they are truly detailed instructions to a bidder; they guide him in soliciting information concerning discrepancies in the contract documents and provide him with all the information necessary to execute the bid form. The Instructions to Bidders consist of these essential elements:

1. Form of Bid: Identify the form of bid and indicate the number of copies to be submitted.

2. Preparation of Bid: Describe which blank spaces in the bid form are to be filled in by the bidder, including base bids, alternates, unit prices, etc.
3. Submission of Bid: State how bids are to be sealed, addressed, and delivered.
4. Examination of Documents and Site: Instruct bidder to examine the contract documents and the site of the proposed project in order to familiarize himself with all aspects of the project.
5. Interpretation of Documents: State how discrepancies in contract documents discovered by bidders will be interpreted and resolved by the architect.
6. Withdrawal and Modification of Bids: State how bids may be withdrawn or modified prior to bid opening.
7. Award of Contract: Describe the procedure under which the award of the contract will be made.
8. Rejection of Bids: State the conditions under which the bids may be rejected.
9. Other Instructions to Bidders: State whether certain information relative to financial status, subcontractor, and substitutions are to be submitted with the bid form.

Bid Form

The Bid Form, sometimes termed the Proposal Form or Form of Proposal, is a document prepared by the architect or issuing agency in order to assure similarity in the preparation and presentation of bids by bidders and to obtain a uniform basis of comparison. By using only the forms prepared by the issuing agency, the owner is assured that all bidders are submitting proposals on an equal basis.

The Bid Form is prepared in the form of a letter from the bidder to the owner, and contains the necessary blank spaces for the bidder to fill in contract prices as well as spaces for the required signatures and addresses.

The Bid Form consists of these essential elements:

1. Addressee: State the name and address of individual receiving bids.

2. Name and Address of Bidder: State the name of the organization and address of the bidder.

3. Project Identification: State the name of the project.

4. Acknowledgement: Provide an enumeration of the documents

and a statement to the effect that the site has been visited and examined.

5. Bid Schedule: Set forth a bid list of all the major bid proposals.

6. Alternates: Set forth a list of all alternate prices. A description of the alternates should be set forth under Division 1, General Requirements.

7. Unit Prices: Provide a list of unit prices and their description.

8. Time of Completion: Establish the time of completion or permit the bidder to insert his own time of completion.

9. Acknowledgement of Addena: Provide spaces for acknowledgement of receipt of addenda by bidders.

10. Agreement to Accept Contract: State the conditions under which the bidder agrees to enter into a formal contract within a specified time.

11. Signature and Address of Bidder: Provide spaces to be filled in by bidder for his signature, address, and seal where necessary.

Sample forms for the Invitation to Bid, the Instructions to Bidders, and the Bid Form are set forth, as follows:

<u>INVITATION TO BID</u>

January 1, 1967

John Jones, Architect
123 Main Street
New York, New York

LIBRARY BUILDING
FIRST AVENUE & MAIN STREET
NEW YORK, NEW YORK

1. Sealed bids for the construction of the above project for the City of New York will be received by the office of John Jones, Architect, until 1:00 P.M., E.S.T., February 1, 1967, (and then publicly opened).

2. In general, the building is a two story structure including a basement, and is approximately 75 feet by 200 feet in size. The frame and slabs are reinforced concrete and the exterior consists of an aluminum curtain wall.

3. (Bids will be based on a single lump sum contract.) Bids will be received for segregated contracts consisting of General Construction; Plumbing; Heating, Ventilating and Air Conditioning; and Electrical Work.

4. Contract Documents may be examined on and after January 1, 1967 at the office of the Architect and at the following Builders' Exchanges:

   a.
   b.
   c.

5. Contract Documents may be obtained at the office of the Architect on or after January 1, 1967 by depositing a check in the amount of $_____ per set, payable to the Architect. Deposits will be refunded to Bidders who return the documents in good condition within 10 days after the opening of bids.

6. Bid security in the form of a Bid Bond or certified check made payable to the City of New York, in an amount equal to 5% of the bid will be required. No Bidder may withdraw his bid within 30 days after the actual date of the opening thereof.

7. Guaranty Bonds in the form of a Performance Bond and a Labor and Materials Payment Bond in an amount equal to 100% of the bid will be required.

INSTRUCTIONS TO BIDDERS

1. **BID FORM**
   Attention is directed to the fact that these Specifications include a copy of Bid Form. This is for the information and convenience of Bidders and is not to be detached from the specifications, or filled out or executed. Separate duplicate copies of the Bid Form are to be submitted by the Bidder for that purpose as set forth below.

2. **PREPARATION OF BID**
   a. Bids shall be submitted in duplicate on Bid Forms which will be furnished by the Architect.
   b. Spaces are provided in the Bid Form for Base Bid and various unit and alternate prices. All such spaces shall be filled in on typewriter or in ink by the Bidder. Where both written works and numerical figures are given, the written words will apply in the event of conflict.

3. **SUBMISSION OF BIDS**
   a. Bids will be received at the time and place set forth in the Invitation to Bid.
   b. Envelopes containing bids shall be sealed, mailed and addressed as follows:

   > Mr. John Jones, Architect
   > 123 Main Street
   > New York, New York

   Mark in lower left hand corner "Bid for Construction of Library Building."

4. **EXAMINATION OF SITE, DOCUMENTS, ETC.**
   Each Bidder shall visit the site of the proposed work and fully acquaint himself with conditions as they exist so that he may fully understand the facilities, difficulties, and restrictions attending the execution of the work under the contract. Bidders shall also thoroughly examine and be familiar with the drawings and the specifications. The failure or omission of any Bidder to receive or examine any form, instrument or document or to visit the site and acquaint himself with conditions there existing shall in no way relieve the Bidder from any obligation with respect to his bid.

5. **INTERPRETATION OF DOCUMENTS**
   No oral interpretations will be made to any Bidder as to the meaning of the drawings and specifications. Every request for such an interpretation shall be made in writing and addressed and forwarded to the Architect. No inquiry received within 5 days of the date fixed for opening of bids will be given consideration. Every interpretation made to

a Bidder will be in the form of an Addendum to the Contract Documents which, if issued, will be sent as promptly as is practicable to all persons to whom the Contract Documents have been issued. All such Addenda shall become part of the Contract Documents.

6. WITHDRAWAL AND MODIFICATION OF BIDS
   a. Bids may be withdrawn on written or telegraphic request received from Bidders prior to the time fixed for opening.
   b. Telegraphic bids will not be considered, but modifications by telegraph or in writing will be considered if received prior to the hour set for opening.

7. AWARD OF CONTRACT
   a. The contract will be awarded to the lowest responsible Bidder on the basis of low bid and accepted alternates.
   or a. The Owner reserves the right to award the contract on any basis he deems to his best interests.

8. REJECTION OF BIDS
   The Owner reserves the right to reject any or all bids, when such rejection is in the interest of the Owner.

9. OTHER INSTRUCTIONS TO BIDDERS
   a. Bid security in the type and amount stated in the Invitation to Bid shall accompany the bid. The bid security shall be retained by the Owner if the Bidder fails to execute the contract, or fails to provide satisfactory Performance and Payment Bonds as required, within ten days after notice of award is mailed to the Bidder.
   b. A financial statement on the form provided by the Architect shall accompany the bid (may be used where required).

<u>BID FORM</u>

To: John Jones, Architect
     123 Main Street   Dated_____
     New York, New York

From: _____(Name of Bidder)
      _____(Address of Bidder)
      _____

For: Construction of Library Building
      First Avenue and Main Street
      New York, New York

The Undersigned, having visited the site of proposed construction of the above noted project, and having familiarized himself with local conditions affecting the cost of the work and with all requirements of Contract Documents as prepared by Architect, and all Addenda to said Documents, hereby proposes to furnish all things as required by said Documents and Addenda thereto for the construction of said Library Building for the following amounts:

B I D   S C H E D U L E

<u>BASE BID</u>

_____
_____Dollars ($_____)

<u>ALTERNATES</u>

The Undersigned will include the following Alternates as described in Section 1--for the following amounts:

	<u>ADD</u>	<u>DEDUCT</u>	<u>NO CHANGE</u>
Alternate No. 1	$_____	$_____	$_____
Alternate No. 2	$_____	$_____	$_____

<u>UNIT PRICES</u>

Should additional work of the following categories be required, adjustment will be made to the Contract Sum at the following unit prices, which shall include all expenses, including overhead and profit. Should less work be required, the unit price will be 15% less than the price quoted for the additional work.

<u>Description</u>	<u>Unit Price</u>
(a) General Machine excavation, removed from site, per cu. yd.	$_____
(b) Machine trench excavation, removed from site, per cu. yd.	$_____
(c) Backfill due to extra excavation, per cu. yd.	$_____

88

(d) Forms for concrete work, includ-
    ing stripping, per square foot $_____

TIME OF COMPLETION

If awarded this contract, the undersigned will complete the
work within_____calendar days from the date of
the notice to proceed. (Note: Bidder shall insert time of completion.)

ADDENDUM RECEIPT

Receipt of the following Addenda to the Contract Documents are
acknowledged:

Addendum No._____   Dated_____
Addendum No._____   Dated_____

BID ACCEPTANCE

                                 Dated_____

If written notice of the acceptance of this Bid is mailed,
telegraphed, or delivered to the Undersigned within 30 days
after the date for opening of Bids or any time thereafter before this bid is withdrawn, the Undersigned will, within ten
(10) days after the date of such mailing, telegraphing, or
delivery of such notice, execute and deliver A.I.A., Contract
Form No. A-101, and furnish Performance and Payment Bond, in
accordance with the specifications and Bid as accepted.

The Undersigned hereby designates as his office to which such
notice of acceptance may be mailed, telegraphed, or delivered:
Name of Bidder:_____
Bidder is: Individual ( ) Partnership ( ) Corporation ( )
            Check one, as case may be.

Residence of Bidder (if individual)_____

Date of Bid_____

    If Bidder is a partnership, fill in the following blanks:
Name of Partners:

_____   _____

_____   _____

    If Bidder is a Corporation, fill in the following blanks:
Organized under the laws of the State of_____
Name and Home Address of the President_____

_____

Name and Home Address of Treasurer_____

_____

11

GENERAL CONDITIONS

General Conditions in essence consist of those provisions which establish and pertain to the legal responsibilities and relationships between the parties involved in the work, namely the owner, the contractor and the architect or engineer.

The American Institute of Architects as well as the Consulting Engineers Council have standard preprinted general conditions for use in private work. The Federal Government (specifically, the General Services Administration), the several states, and many cities and municipalities likewise have standard preprinted general conditions for use on public work.

Any architect, and especially a beginner, would be well advised to use the standard "General Conditions of the AIA" for a private project, or those of a governmental agency if his commission involves a public project. This admonition is based on the fact that the language of the preprinted standard has stood the test of time. There are, in addition, several advantages to using general conditions of long standing. A history of use is accompanied by precedents established in the courts. The terms are familiar to the contractor as well as to the architect. A standard document provides assurance that most major contractual-legal provisions are included.

The first edition of the AIA "General Conditions" was published in 1911. Prior to that time, a document known as the "Uniform Contract," originated in 1888, was used. This earlier document was a preprinted contract form designed for use as the contractual agreement between the owner and the contractor. In 1911, this Uniform Contract was divided into the two parts that are familiar to us today: the Agreement (the Standard Form of Agreement between Contractor and Owner for Construction of Buildings, AIA Document No. A-101), and General Conditions of the Contract for Construction (AIA Document No. A-201). The latter, commonly referred to as the General Conditions, has undergone many revisions since 1911. The current issue is the Tenth Edition, dated September 1966. (See sample at end of chapter.)

In addition to articles pertaining to the legal responsibilities and relationships between the parties to the contract, there are non-technical requirements in the AIA "General Conditions," such as provisions for submissions of shop drawings and samples, copies of drawings and specifications, cash allowances, cutting and patching, and cleaning-up.

It has also been necessary to modify the standard General Conditions to suit the requirements for a specific project. These modifications, in the form of additions, deletions, and substitutions are called Supplementary Conditions. However, in the process of modification, the Supplementary Conditions have become larded with many articles that are, in essence, work of a general nature to be performed by the Contractor in order to construct the building, and not necessarily a contractual-legal responsibility. These articles have included temporary facilities (roads, offices, fences, scaffolding, toilets, watchmen), signs, photographs, and temporary utilities (water, heat, electricity).

Until the advent of the CSI Format for Construction Specifications, there was little choice but to add these non-legal requirements to the Supplementary Conditions. Now with the CSI Format, the modifications to the legal requirements of the Standard AIA General Conditions can be taken care of in the Supplementary Conditions, while the non-technical work requirements can be included under Division 1, General Requirements. (See Chapter 17 for the scope of sections covered under Division 1.)

The current edition of the AIA General Conditions reflects the radical change effected through the reduction of 44 articles to 14 articles. This has been accomplished by grouping under common article headings certain related information previously under separate articles. While this first major improvement is a step in the right direction, since it codifies the location of information, it nonetheless retains several articles of other than legal-contractual character that could well be placed under Division 1 of the Uniform System.

While this book is limited to the subject of technical construction specifications and cannot presume to offer expertise on legal matters, it can forewarn architects and engineers about the use of General Conditions and their modifications. The most important reason for having a document to cover only the legal responsibilities and relationships of the parties is that architects are not in the business of practicing law. Under no circumstances should they draw up or modify any legal provisions unless, upon so doing, these forms are forwarded to the owner and the owner's attorney for checking and approval. To protect the architect, responsibility for these legal forms and their modifications must, in turn, be accepted in writing by the owner and his attorney. Otherwise, if the architect collects his fee and subsequently trouble develops on the project for which he has drawn the contract, he may have been guilty of having practiced law illegally.

By limiting the articles in the General Conditions to those having only to do with the legal responsibilities and relationships, and having the owner acknowledge his responsibility in connection with them, the architect can then develop the other nontechnical provisions in the General Requirements for which he is qualified by his training and expertise. The architect is likewise cautioned with respect to the insurance provisions contained in the General Conditions. In amending the article pertaining to insurance (see Article 11 of AIA Doc. A-201 illustrated herein), the architect should consult with the owner's insurance advisors to assure that the insurance provisions adequately protect the contractor and architect as well as the owner.

It has been the practice of some architects to include the standard preprinted General Conditions by reference only, thereby making it a part of the contract documents. It is recommended however, that a physical copy of the General Conditions be bound into the specifications, since there is frequent reference to this document during the course of construction.

For the small project, the AIA Document No. A-201 is considered by many architects to be both too voluminous and too comprehensive, including many articles that are not appropriate nor essential to the project. To obviate the necessity of drastically amending AIA Document No. A-201 in the Supplementary Conditions, the AIA has developed a combination Agreement and General Conditions known as the AIA Short Form for Small Construction Projects, AIA Document No. A-107, a copy of which is illustrated in this chapter.

For information on other standard preprinted General Conditions, the reader is directed to the following associations from whom copyrighted general conditions can be purchased:

American Association of State Highway Officials
917 National Press Building
Washington, D.C.

American Public Works Association
1313 East 60 Street
Chicago, Illinois 60637

American Society of Civil Engineers
345 East 47 Street
New York, N.Y. 10017

Associated General Contractors of America
1957 E Street N.W.
Washington, D.C. 20006

Consulting Engineers Council
1155 15th Street N.W.
Washington, D.C. 20005

To modify the AIA General Conditions, the architect issues a document entitled Supplementary Conditions. Some architects accomplish this by affixing additional articles to the 14 standard articles, commencing with number 15 and continuing on through all his modifications. Others start the Supplementary Conditions with number 1 and continue in numerical sequence with modifications to the General Conditions, even though the number bears no relationship to the article number. It is recommended that the General Conditions and the Supplementary Conditions be made a part of the Contract Documents by incorporating the following sample text in the bound book of specifications, and continuing in this manner:

GENERAL CONDITIONS

1. GENERAL CONDITIONS.

"The General Conditions of the Contract for Construction," American Institute of Architects Document No. A-201, tenth edition, September 1966, hereinafter referred to as the General Conditions, a copy of which is bound herein, shall become a part of the Contract Documents.

2. SUPPLEMENTARY CONDITIONS

The following Supplementary Conditions contain modifications to the AIA General Conditions in the form of additions, deletions and substitutions. Where any part of the AIA General Conditions is so modified by the Supplementary Conditions, the unaltered provisions shall remain in effect.

    a. Article 1. Contract Documents
      1. Par. 1.1 Definitions. Add the following subparagraph:

        "1.1.5 Days: The term day shall mean a calendar day of 24 hours commencing at 12:00 midnight. The term working day shall mean any calendar day except Saturdays, Sundays and legal holidays at the site of the Project."

2. Par. 1.2 Execution, Correlation, Intent and Interpretations. Add the following to subparagraph 1.2.3:

"The following shall constitute the order of precedence in the event that there is a conflict between the Contract Documents:
   Agreement
   General Conditions
   Supplementary Conditions
   Specifications
   Drawings.
   Note: The above sequence has been used by some specifiers but is not an AIA condition.

Large scale details on drawings shall take precedence over scale measurements. Where duplications are encountered in the specifications, the most expensive material or method of construction shall take precedence."

3. Par. 1.3 Copies Furnished and Ownership. Modify subparagraph 1.3.1 as follows:

"A total of ____ copies of the Contract Documents will be furnished, free of charge. Additional copies of the Contract Documents may be obtained by the Contractor at his expense at the cost of reproduction."

b. Article 2. Architect
   (Note: Further modifications to the General Conditions may be made following the outline suggested above.)

It would be wise to consult with attorneys and insurance counselors whenever the standard general conditions are to be modified. In addition there are several sources of information on this · subject that are available as follows:

Architects' Handbook of Professional Practice
The American Institute of Architects
1735 New York Avenue, N.W.
Washington, D. C. 20006

Architectural and Engineering Law, Second Edition
Bernard Tomson & Norman Coplan
Reinhold Publishing Corporation
430 Park Avenue
New York, N. Y. 10022

The AIA Standard Contract Forms and the Law
Parker and Adams
Little, Brown & Co.
Boston, Mass.

Architectural Practice
Cowgill and Small
Reinhold Publishing Corp.
430 Park Avenue
New York, N. Y. 10022

Legal Responsibilities in the Practice of Architecture and Engineering
John R. Clark, Partner
Dechert, Price & Rhoads, Attorneys
3 Penn Center Plaza
Philadelphia, Penn.

Insurance   There are many risks and liabilities involved in the construction of a project which are of concern to the architect. The AIA General Conditions, Article 11, deals with some insurance requirements, but does not include amounts nor many other insurance coverages that may be necessary to safeguard the interests of all the parties to the contract, including the architect. Obviously, the contractor has the prime responsibility, but the owner and the architect may have contingent liability, and to safeguard them they may be added to some insurance policies as additional insured.

The AIA General Conditions should be modified to include the policy limits which the contractor should be required to furnish. These limits will vary with the size and character of the project and with its location, and should be consistent with the inherent risks involved. The modifications may also include other types of insurance coverage, as may be determined by the owner and his attorney and insurance advisor.

In order to ascertain that the insurance specified is in force and effect on the project, the architect requires that a certificate of insurance listing all pertinent data be furnished by the contractor's insurance company. Since each insurance company issues its own certificate, and since they differ in form, it is often difficult to readily understand what is stated in a certificate without a careful analysis of each entry.

To assure ready evaluation and analysis of insurance, the AIA has prepared a special certificate form, Document No. G705 (sample illustrated at end of chapter) which provides for the listing of policy numbers, inception, and expiration dates, and for the limits of liability under the various categories.

The AIA, through its Committee on Insurance, has developed a checklist on protection, and owner's instructions regarding insurance.

The owner should determine the types and amounts of insurance he will carry and those that the contractor will be required to carry. The architect should request written confirmation of the owner's decisions and include this information in the Supplementary Conditions. To guide the architect in obtaining a clear expression of the owner's decisions, the following set of prototype letter texts is suggested by the AIA. These should be prepared in accordance with the needs of the particular project involved.

Your instructions are requested concerning the insurance provisions to be incorporated in the Contract Documents for the proposed construction project.

Architect's Request to Owner

The contract specifications will require the Contractor to carry certain forms of insurance such as Workmen's Compensation, Public Liability, Property Damage and Automobile Liability. For your convenience, Enclosure "A" may be used to instruct us regarding the limits and kinds of coverage which you wish specified.

There are certain other insurance coverages which are usually the responsibility of the Owner such as Builder's Risk Fire and Extended Coverage or all Physical Loss; Owner's Contingent Liability Insurance, etc. Your instructions to us in connection with these coverages can be indicated on Enclosure "B".

We suggest you consult your insurance counselor concerning the limits and kinds of insurance that should be provided to insure the project adequately. We will be glad to supply any additional information which he may require. Please advise us as soon as possible in order that we may complete the Contract Documents.

ENCLOSURE A

Owners Instructions to Architect Regarding Contractor's Insurance

You are hereby instructed to require the following kinds and amounts of insurance in the specifications for the subject project. The Contractor, as part of the Contract cost, shall provide and maintain insurance as follows, in companies acceptable to the Owner.

1) *Workmen's Compensation* as required by all applicable Federal, State, Maritime or other laws including Employers Liability with a limit of at least: $_____

2) *Comprehensive General Liability* including Contractual Liability; Contingent Liability; Explosion; Collapse and Underground Drainage; Damage; Occurrence Basis Bodily Injury; Broad Form Personal Injury; Broad Form Property Damage; and Completed Operations to be kept in force for at least two years after the work has been completed: $_____

3) *Comprehensive Automobile Liability* including non-ownership and hired car coverage as well as owned vehicles: $_____

> *Bodily Injury*
> Each Person $_____
> Each Occurrence $_____
>
> *Property Damage*
> Each Occurrence $_____

4) *Bonds or Other Insurance* which we require the Contractor to provide:

Kind	Amount

The Contractor shall furnish the Owner with satisfactory evidence of the required Insurance and / or Bonds with a provision that at least fifteen days prior written notice will be given to the Owner in event of cancellation or material change.

ENCLOSURE B

Owner's Instruction to Architect Regarding Owner's Insurance

You are hereby instructed to indicate in the specifications that the Owner will provide the following kinds of insurance for the subject project:

1) *Owner's Contingent Liability* (see Article ____ of the General Conditions.)

2) *Builder's Risk or All Physical Loss* on the completed value form to the full insurable value of the work in the names of the Owner and all Contractors as their interests may appear (see Article ____ of the General Conditions.)

3) *Other Insurance* (state kind and amount.)

To obtain additional information on insurance, the architect and the beginner is directed to the following sources:

Insurance for Contractors
Walter T. Derk
Fred S. James & Co.
1 North LaSalle Street
Chicago, Illinois

Engineering Contracts and Specifications
Robert W. Abbett
John Wiley & Sons
New York, N. Y.

In order to familiarize the architect with some of the terms used in insurance, the following is an encyclopedia of insurance terms:

Accident: A sudden, unexpected event identifiable as to time and place of occurrence.

Bodily injury: Pertaining to the body; generally, a physical injury.

Builders Risk Insurance: Coverage for a loss resulting from the hazards of fire and lightning, extended coverage to a building during the course of construction.

Care Custody and Control (CCC) Exclusion: A standard exclusion in liability policies for damage to property:
  (1) in the care, custody or control of the insured,
  (2) owned, occupied by or rented to the insured,
  (3) over which the insured for any purpose is exercising physical control,

(4) used by the insured (except liability under insured Railroad Sidetrack Agreements).

Although it is occasionally modified or eliminated, proper coverage such as Builder's Risk or Installation Floater is generally used in place of modifications.

Certificate: A statement issued by an insurance company evidencing that an insurance policy has been issued. It states the policy number, coverage, limits, effective and expiration dates, etc.

Completed Operations Insurance: Coverage for accidents which occur after the operations have been either completed and turned over to the Owner or abandoned.

Comprehensive General Liability Insurance: A liability policy which automatically includes all forms of general (as differentiated from specific forms such as aircraft, marine, auto, etc.) liability, the source of which may be either tort or contract. Policy may exclude Products or Completed Operations, Property Damage and most forms of contractual liabilities.

Employers Liability Insurance: Protection for the Employer against common lawsuits by employees for damages which may arise out of injuries or diseases in the course of their work. Limit of liability is per accident not per employee.

Fire Legal Liability: Liability imposed by law for loss of or damage to property of others in the care, custody, or control of the insured and caused by fire.

Hazard Insurance: Coverage for a condition which creates the possibility of a loss; *e.g.*, ownership or use of premises, elevators, conduct of operations. The term is also used to designate the divisions of a liability insurance policy.

Hold Harmless or Contractual Liability: Liability assumed by a party under a written contract. The degree of liability assumed is generally described as Limited, Intermediate, or Broad Form. (The following examples of hold-harmless clauses are given only to illustrate the degree of liability assumed under each form and are not intended to be used as written. Consult an insurance counselor for the proper form and wording.)

Limited Form: "To indemnify and save harmless the Owner with respect to liability imposed upon said Owner by law, but only to the extent that such liability arises out of the sole negligence of the named insured and out of work performed by the named insured under its Contract with the Owner."

Intermediate Form: "To indemnify and save harmless the Owner with respect to liability imposed upon said Owner by law but only to the extent that such liability arises out of the sole negligence of the named insured or the joint or concurring negligence of the named insured and the Owner, and out of the operations of the named insured under its Contract with the Owner."

Broad Form: "To indemnify and save harmless the Owner with respect to the liability imposed upon said Owner by law but only to the extent that such liability arises out of the operations of the named insured under its Contract with the Owner."

Negligence: Failure to use that degree of care which a reasonable and prudent person would ordinarily use under the circumstances in a particular case. Negligence may involve acts of commission, omission or both.

Occurrence: A happening or a continuous or repeated exposure to conditions which result in injury or damage, provided the injury or damage is accidentally caused.

Personal injury: Injury or damage to the character of a person as opposed to the body. Personal injury may arise from false arrest, slander, libel, malicious prosecution, etc.

USL&HW Compensation Act: The United States Longshoremen's and Harbor Workers.

Compensation Act: This legislation covers maritime employment on navigable waters other than Master or members of the crew. The coverage is provided by an endorsement to the Workmen's Compensation policy.

Water Damage Legal Liability: Liability imposed by law for loss of or damage to property of others caused by the accidental discharge, leakage or overflow of water on or from premises owned by or rented to the insured. The usual Care, Custody, and Control exclusions apply.

X C U: Symbols which refer to exclusions of coverage for property damage arising out of (1) blasting or explosion, (2) collapse of or structural injury to any building or structure, and (3) damage to underground property caused by and occurring during the use of mechanical equipment.

THE AMERICAN INSTITUTE OF ARCHITECTS

This form is reproduced
by permission of the copyright owner,
The American Institute of Architects

AIA Document A201

General Conditions of the Contract for Construction

TABLE OF ARTICLES

INDEX

ARTICLE 1

CONTRACT DOCUMENTS

1.1 DEFINITIONS

1.1.1 THE CONTRACT DOCUMENTS

The Contract Documents consist of the Agreement, the Conditions of the Contract (General, Supplementary and other Conditions), the Drawings, the Specifications, all Addenda issued prior to execution of the Agreement, and all Modifications thereto. A Modification is (1) a written amendment to the Contract signed by both parties, (2) a Change Order, (3) a written interpretation issued by the Architect pursuant to Subparagraph 1.2.5, or (4) a written order for a minor change in the Work issued by the Architect pursuant to Paragraph 12.3. A Modification may be made only after execution of the Contract.

1.1.2 THE CONTRACT

The Contract Documents form the Contract. The Contract represents the entire and integrated agreement between the parties hereto and supersedes all prior negotiations, representations, or agreements, either written or oral, including the bidding documents. The Contract may be amended or modified only by a Modification as defined in Subparagraph 1.1.1.

1.1.3 THE WORK

The term Work includes all labor necessary to produce the construction required by the Contract Documents, and all materials and equipment incorporated or to be incorporated in such construction.

1.1.4 THE PROJECT

The Project is the total construction designed by the Architect of which the Work performed under the Contract Documents may be the whole or a part.

1.2 EXECUTION, CORRELATION, INTENT AND INTERPRETATIONS

1.2.1 The Contract Documents shall be signed in not less than triplicate by the Owner and Contractor. If either the Owner or the Contractor or both do not sign the Conditions of the Contract, Drawings, Specifications, or any of the other Contract Documents, the Architect shall identify them.

1.2.2 By executing the Contract, the Contractor represents that he has visited the site, familiarized himself with the local conditions under which the Work is to be performed, and correlated his observations with the requirements of the Contract Documents.

1.2.3 The Contract Documents are complementary, and what is required by any one shall be as binding as if required by all. The intention of the Documents is to include all labor, materials, equipment and other items as provided in Subparagraph 4.4.1 necessary for the proper execution and completion of the Work, and also to include those things which may be reasonably inferable from the Contract Documents as being necessary to produce the intended results. Words which have well-known technical or trade meanings are used herein in accordance with such recognized meanings.

1.2.4 The organization of the Specifications into divisions, sections and articles, and the arrangement of Drawings shall not control the Contractor in dividing the Work among Subcontractors or in establishing the extent of Work to be performed by any trade.

1.2.5 Written interpretations necessary for the proper execution or progress of the Work, in the form of drawings or otherwise, will be issued with reasonable promptness by the Architect and in accordance with any schedule agreed upon. Such interpretations shall be consistent with and reasonably inferable from the Contract Documents, and may be effected by Field Order.

1.3 COPIES FURNISHED AND OWNERSHIP

1.3.1 Unless otherwise provided in the Contract Documents, the Contractor will be furnished, free of charge, all copies of Drawings and Specifications reasonably necessary for the execution of the Work.

1.3.2 All Drawings, Specifications and copies thereof furnished by the Architect are and shall remain his property. They are not to be used on any other project, and, with the exception of one contract set for each party to the Contract, are to be returned to the Architect on request at the completion of the Work.

ARTICLE 2

ARCHITECT

2.1 DEFINITION

2.1.1 The Architect is the person or organization identified as such in the Agreement and is referred to throughout the Contract Documents as if singular in number and masculine in gender. The term Architect means the Architect or his authorized representative.

2.1.2 Nothing contained in the Contract Documents shall create any contractual relationship between the Architect and the Contractor.

2.2 ADMINISTRATION OF THE CONTRACT

2.2.1 The Architect will provide general administration of the Contract, including performance of the functions hereinafter described.

2.2.2 The Architect will be the Owner's representative during construction and until final payment. The Architect will have authority to act on behalf of the Owner to the extent provided in the Contract Documents, unless otherwise modified by written instrument which will be shown to the Contractor. The Architect will advise and consult with the Owner, and all of the Owner's instructions to the Contractor shall be issued through the Architect.

2.2.3 The Architect shall at all times have access to the Work wherever it is in preparation and progress. The Contractor shall provide facilities for such access so the Architect may perform his functions under the Contract Documents.

2.2.4 The Architect will make periodic visits to the site to familiarize himself generally with the progress and quality of the Work and to determine in general if the Work is proceeding in accordance with the Contract Documents. On the basis of his on-site observations as an architect, he will keep the Owner informed of the progress of the Work, and will endeavor to guard the Owner against defects and deficiencies in the Work of the Contractor. The Architect will not be required to make exhaustive or continuous on-site inspections to check the quality or quantity of the Work. The Architect will not be responsible for construction means, methods, techniques, sequences or procedures, or for safety precautions and programs in connection with the Work, and he will not be responsible for the Contractor's failure to carry out the Work in accordance with the Contract Documents.

2.2.5 Based on such observations and the Contractor's Applications for Payment, the Architect will determine the amounts owing to the Contractor and will issue Certificates for Payment in such amounts, as provided in Paragraph 9.4.

2.2.6 The Architect will be, in the first instance, the interpreter of the requirements of the Contract Documents and the judge of the performance thereunder by both the Owner and Contractor. The Architect will, within a reasonable time, render such interpretations as he may deem necessary for the proper execution or progress of the Work.

2.2.7 Claims, disputes and other matters in question between the Contractor and the Owner relating to the execution or progress of the Work or the interpretation of the Contract Documents shall be referred initially to the Architect for decision which he will render in writing within a reasonable time.

2.2.8 All interpretations and decisions of the Architect shall be consistent with the intent of the Contract Documents. In his capacity as interpreter and judge, he will exercise his best efforts to insure faithful performance by both the Owner and the Contractor and will not show partiality to either.

2.2.9 The Architect's decisions in matters relating to artistic effect will be final if consistent with the intent of the Contract Documents.

2.2.10 Any claim, dispute or other matter that has been referred to the Architect, except those relating to artistic effect as provided in Subparagraph 2.2.9 and except any which have been waived by the making or acceptance of final payment as provided in Subparagraphs 9.7.5. and 9.7.6, shall be subject to arbitration upon the written demand of either party. However, no demand for arbitra-

tion of any such claim, dispute or other matter may be made until the earlier of:

> **.1** the date on which the Architect has rendered his decision, or
>
> **.2** the tenth day after the parties have presented their evidence to the Architect if he has not rendered his written decision by that date.

2.2.11 If a decision of the Architect is made in writing and states that it is final but subject to appeal, no demand for arbitration of a claim, dispute or other matter covered by such decision may be made later than thirty days after the date on which the party making the demand received the decision. The failure to demand arbitration within said thirty days' period will result in the Architect's decision becoming final and binding upon the Owner and the Contractor. If the Architect renders a decision after arbitration proceedings have been initiated, such decision may be entered as evidence but will not supersede any arbitration proceedings except where the decision is acceptable to the parties concerned.

2.2.12 The Architect will have authority to reject Work which does not conform to the Contract Documents. Whenever, in his reasonable opinion, he considers it necessary or advisable to insure the proper implementation of the intent of the Contract Documents, he will have authority to require the Contractor to stop the Work or any portion thereof, or to require special inspection or testing of the Work as provided in Subparagraph 7.8.2 whether or not such Work be then fabricated, installed or completed. However, neither the Architect's authority to act under this Subparagraph 2.2.12, nor any decision made by him in good faith either to exercise or not to exercise such authority, shall give rise to any duty or responsibility of the Architect to the Contractor, any Subcontractor, any of their agents or employees, or any other person performing any of the Work.

2.2.13 The Architect will review Shop Drawings and Samples as provided in Subparagraphs 4.13.1 through 4.13.8 inclusive.

2.2.14 The Architect will prepare Change Orders in accordance with Article 12, and will have authority to order minor changes in the Work as provided in Subparagraph 12.3.1.

2.2.15 The Architect will conduct inspections to determine the dates of Substantial Completion and final completion, will receive written guarantees and related documents required by the Contract and assembled by the Contractor, and will issue a final Certificate for Payment.

2.2.16 If the Owner and Architect agree, the Architect will provide one or more full-time Project Representatives to assist the Architect in carrying out his responsibilities at the site. The duties, responsibilities and limitations of authority of any such Project Representative shall be as set forth in an exhibit to be incorporated in the Contract Documents.

2.2.17 The duties, responsibilities and limitations of authority of the Architect as the Owner's representative during construction as set forth in Articles 1 through 14 inclusive of these General Conditions will not be modified or extended without written consent of the Owner and the Architect which will be shown to the Contractor.

2.2.18 The Architect will not be responsible for the acts or omissions of the Contractor, or any Subcontractors, or any of his or their agents or employees, or any other persons performing any of the Work.

2.2.19 In case of the termination of the employment of the Architect, the Owner shall appoint an architect against whom the Contractor makes no reasonable objection, whose status under the Contract Documents shall be that of the former architect. Any dispute in connection with such appointment shall be subject to arbitration.

ARTICLE 3

OWNER

3.1 DEFINITION

3.1.1 The Owner is the person or organization identified as such in the Agreement and is referred to throughout the Contract Documents as if singular in number and masculine in gender. The term Owner means the Owner or his authorized representative.

3.2 INFORMATION AND SERVICES REQUIRED OF THE OWNER

3.2.1 The Owner shall furnish all surveys describing the physical characteristics, legal limits and utility locations for the site of the Project.

3.2.2 The Owner shall secure and pay for easements for permanent structures or permanent changes in existing facilities.

3.2.3 Information or services under the Owner's control shall be furnished by the Owner with reasonable promptness to avoid delay in the orderly progress of the Work.

3.2.4 The Owner shall issue all instructions to the Contractor through the Architect.

3.2.5 The foregoing are in addition to other duties and responsibilities of the Owner enumerated herein and especially those in respect to Payment and Insurance in Articles 9 and 11 respectively.

ARTICLE 4

CONTRACTOR

4.1 DEFINITION

4.1.1 The Contractor is the person or organization identified as such in the Agreement and is referred to throughout the Contract Documents as if singular in number and masculine in gender. The term Contractor means the Contractor or his authorized representative.

4.2 REVIEW OF CONTRACT DOCUMENTS

4.2.1 The Contractor shall carefully study and compare the Agreement, Conditions of the Contract, Drawings, Specifications, Addenda and Modifications and shall at once report to the Architect any error, inconsistency or omission he may discover; but the Contractor shall not be liable to the Owner or the Architect for any damage resulting from any such errors, inconsistencies or omissions. The Contractor shall do no Work without proper Drawings and Specifications.

4.3 SUPERVISION AND CONSTRUCTION PROCEDURES

4.3.1 The Contractor shall supervise and direct the Work, using his best skill and attention. He shall be solely responsible for all construction means, methods, techniques, sequences and procedures and for coordinating all portions of the Work under the Contract.

4.4 LABOR AND MATERIALS

4.4.1 Unless otherwise specifically noted, the Contractor shall provide and pay for all labor, materials, equipment, tools, construction equipment and machinery, water, heat, utilities, transportation, and other facilities and services necessary for the proper execution and completion of the Work.

4.4.2 The Contractor shall at all times enforce strict discipline and good order among his employees and shall not employ on the Work any unfit person or anyone not skilled in the task assigned to him.

4.5 WARRANTY AND GUARANTEE

4.5.1 The Contractor warrants and guarantees to the Owner and the Architect that all materials and equipment incorporated in the Project will be new unless otherwise specified, and that all Work will be of good quality, free from faults and defects and in conformance with the Contract Documents. All Work not so conforming to these standards may be considered defective by the Owner or the Architect. If required by the Architect, the Contractor shall furnish satisfactory evidence as to the kind and quality of materials and equipment.

4.5.2 The warranties and guarantees provided in this Paragraph 4.5 and elsewhere in the Contract Documents shall be in addition to and not in limitation of any other warranty or guarantee or remedy required by law or by the Contract Documents.

4.6 TAXES

4.6.1 The Contractor shall pay all sales, consumer, use and other similar taxes required by law.

4.7 PERMITS, FEES AND NOTICES

4.7.1 The Contractor shall secure and pay for all permits, fees and licenses necessary for the proper execution and completion of the Work.

4.7.2 The Contractor shall give all notices and comply with all laws, ordinances, rules, regulations and orders of any public authority bearing on the Work. If the Contractor observes that any of the Contract Documents are at variance therewith in any respect, he shall promptly notify the Architect in writing, and any necessary changes shall be adjusted by appropriate Modification. If the Contractor performs any Work knowing it to be contrary to such laws, ordinances, rules and regulations, and without such notice to the Architect, he shall assume full responsibility therefor and shall bear all costs attributable thereto.

4.8 CASH ALLOWANCES

4.8.1 The Contractor shall include in the Contract Sum all allowances stated in the Contract Documents. These allowances shall cover the net cost of the materials and equipment delivered and unloaded at the site, and all applicable taxes. The Contractor's handling costs on the site, labor, installation costs, overhead, profit and other expenses shall be included in the Contract Sum and not in the allowance. The Contractor shall cause the Work covered by these allowances to be performed for such amounts and by such persons as the Architect may direct, but he will not be required to employ persons against whom he makes a reasonable objection. If the cost, when determined, is more than or less than the allowance, the Contract Sum shall be adjusted accordingly by Change Order.

4.9 SUPERINTENDENT

4.9.1 The Contractor shall employ a competent superintendent and necessary assistants who shall be in attendance at the Project site during the progress of the Work. The superintendent and assistants shall be satisfactory to the Architect, and shall not be changed except with the consent of the Architect, unless the superintendent proves to be unsatisfactory to the Contractor and ceases to be in his employ. The superintendent shall represent the Contractor and shall have full authority to act on his behalf. All communications given to the superintendent shall be as binding as if given to the Contractor. Important communications will be confirmed in writing. Other communications will be so confirmed on written request in each case.

4.10 RESPONSIBILITY FOR THOSE PERFORMING THE WORK

4.10.1 The Contractor shall be responsible for the acts and omissions of all his employees and all Subcontractors, their agents and employees, and all other persons performing any of the Work under a contract with the Contractor.

4.11 PROGRESS SCHEDULE

4.11.1 The Contractor, immediately after being awarded the Contract, shall prepare and submit for the Architect's approval an estimated progress schedule for the Work in relation to the entire Project. This schedule shall indicate the dates for the starting and completion of the various stages of construction and, with the Architect's consent, may be revised as required.

4.12 DRAWINGS AND SPECIFICATIONS AT THE SITE

4.12.1 The Contractor shall maintain at the site for the Owner one copy of all Drawings, Specifications, Addenda, approved Shop Drawings, Change Orders and other Modifications, in good order and marked to record all changes made during construction. These shall be available to the Architect and shall be delivered to him for the Owner upon completion of the Work.

4.13 SHOP DRAWINGS AND SAMPLES

4.13.1 Shop Drawings are drawings, diagrams, illustrations, schedules, performance charts, brochures and other data which are prepared by the Contractor or any Subcontractor, manufacturer, supplier or distributor, and which illustrate some portion of the Work.

4.13.2 Samples are physical examples furnished by the Contractor to illustrate materials, equipment or workmanship, and to establish standards by which the Work will be judged.

4.13.3 The Contractor shall review, stamp with his approval and submit, with reasonable promptness and in orderly sequence so as to cause no delay in the Work or in the work of any other contractor, all Shop Drawings and Samples required by the Contract Documents or subsequently by the Architect as covered by Modifications. Shop Drawings and Samples shall be properly identified as specified, or as the Architect may require. At the time of submission the Contractor shall inform the Architect in writing of any deviation in the Shop Drawings or Samples from the requirements of the Contract Documents.

4.13.4 By approving and submitting Shop Drawings and Samples, the Contractor thereby represents that he has determined and verified all field measurements, field construction criteria, materials, catalog numbers and similar data, or will do so, and that he has checked and coordinated each Shop Drawing and Sample with the requirements of the Work and of the Contract Documents.

4.13.5 The Architect will review and approve Shop Drawings and Samples with reasonable promptness so as to cause no delay, but only for conformance with the design concept of the Project and with the information given in the Contract Documents. The Architect's approval of a separate item shall not indicate approval of an assembly in which the item functions.

4.13.6 The Contractor shall make any corrections required by the Architect and shall resubmit the required number of corrected copies of Shop Drawings or new Samples until approved. The Contractor shall direct specific attention in writing or on resubmitted Shop Drawings to revisions other than the corrections requested by the Architect on previous submissions.

4.13.7 The Architect's approval of Shop Drawings or Samples shall not relieve the Contractor of responsibility for any deviation from the requirements of the Contract Documents unless the Contractor has informed the Architect in writing of such deviation at the time of submission and the Architect has given written approval to the specific deviation, nor shall the Architect's approval relieve the Contractor from responsibility for errors or omissions in the Shop Drawings or Samples.

4.13.8 No Work requiring a Shop Drawing or Sample submission shall be commenced until the submission has been approved by the Architect. All such Work shall be in accordance with approved Shop Drawings and Samples.

4.14 USE OF SITE

4.14.1 The Contractor shall confine operations at the site to areas permitted by law, ordinances, permits and the Contract Documents and shall not unreasonably encumber the site with any materials or equipment.

4.15 CUTTING AND PATCHING OF WORK

4.15.1 The Contractor shall do all cutting, fitting or patching of his Work that may be required to make its several parts fit together properly, and shall not endanger any Work by cutting, excavating or otherwise altering the Work or any part of it.

4.16 CLEANING UP

4.16.1 The Contractor at all times shall keep the premises free from accumulation of waste materials or rubbish caused by his operations. At the completion of the Work he shall remove all his waste materials and rubbish from and about the Project as well as all his tools, construction equipment, machinery and surplus materials, and shall clean all glass surfaces and leave the Work "broom-clean" or its equivalent, except as otherwise specified.

4.16.2 If the Contractor fails to clean up, the Owner may do so and the cost thereof shall be charged to the Contractor as provided in Paragraph 7.6.

4.17 COMMUNICATIONS

4.17.1 The Contractor shall forward all communications to the Owner through the Architect.

4.18 INDEMNIFICATION

4.18.1 The Contractor shall indemnify and hold harmless the Owner and the Architect and their agents and employees from and against all claims, damages, losses and expenses including attorneys' fees arising out of or resulting from the performance of the Work, provided that any such claim, damage, loss or expense (a) is attributable to bodily injury, sickness, disease or death, or to injury to or destruction of tangible property (other than the Work itself) including the loss of use resulting therefrom, and (b) is caused in whole or in part by any negligent act or omission of the Contractor, any Subcontractor, anyone directly or indirectly employed by any of them or anyone for whose acts any of them may be liable, regardless of whether or not it is caused in part by a party indemnified hereunder.

4.18.2 In any and all claims against the Owner or the Architect or any of their agents or employees by any employee of the Contractor, any Subcontractor, anyone directly or indirectly employed by any of them or anyone for whose acts any of them may be liable, the indemnification obligation under this Paragraph 4.18 shall not be limited in any way by any limitation on the amount or type of damages, compensation or benefits payable by or for the Contractor or any Subcontractor under workmen's compensation acts, disability benefit acts or other employee benefit acts.

4.18.3 The obligations of the Contractor under this Paragraph 4.18 shall not extend to the liability of the Architect, his agents or employees arising out of (1) the preparation or approval of maps, drawings, opinions, reports, surveys, Change Orders, designs or specifications, or (2) the giving of or the failure to give directions or instructions by the Architect, his agents or employees provided such giving or failure to give is the primary cause of the injury or damage .

ARTICLE 5

SUBCONTRACTORS

5.1 DEFINITION

5.1.1 A Subcontractor is a person or organization who has a direct contract with the Contractor to perform any of the Work at the site. The term Subcontractor is referred to throughout the Contract Documents as if singular in number and masculine in gender and means a Subcontractor or his authorized representative.

5.1.2 A Sub-subcontractor is a person or organization who has a direct or indirect contract with a Subcontractor to perform any of the Work at the site. The term Sub-subcontractor is referred to throughout the Contract Documents as if singular in number and masculine in gender and means a Sub-subcontractor or an authorized representative thereof.

5.1.3 Nothing contained in the Contract Documents shall create any contractual relation between the Owner or the Architect and any Subcontractor or Sub-subcontractor.

5.2 AWARD OF SUBCONTRACTS AND OTHER CONTRACTS FOR PORTIONS OF THE WORK

5.2.1 As soon as practicable after bids are received and prior to the award of the Contract, the successful bidder shall furnish to the Architect in writing for acceptance by the Owner and the Architect a list of the names of the subcontractors or other persons or organizations (including those who are to furnish materials or equipment fabricated to a special design) proposed for such portions of the Work as may be designated in the bidding requirements, or, if none is so designated, the names of the Subcontractors proposed for the principal portions of the Work. Prior to the award of the Contract, the Architect shall notify the successful bidder in writing if either the Owner or the Architect, after due investigation, has reasonable objection to any person or organization on such list. Failure of the Owner or Architect to make an objection to any person or organization on the list prior to the award shall constitute acceptance of such person or organization.

5.2.2 If, prior to the award of the Contract, the Owner or Architect has reasonable objection to and refuses to accept any person or organization on such list, the successful bidder may, prior to the award, withdraw his bid without forfeiture of bid security. If the successful bidder submits an acceptable substitute with an increase in his bid price to cover the difference in cost occasioned by such substitution, the Owner may, at his discretion, accept the increased bid price or he may disqualify the bid. If, after the award, the Owner or Architect refuses to accept any person or organization on such list, the Contractor shall submit an acceptable substitute and the Contract Sum shall be increased or decreased by the difference in cost occasioned by such substitution and an appropriate Change Order shall be issued; however, no increase in the Contract Sum shall be allowed for any such substitution unless the Contractor has acted promptly and responsively in submitting a name with respect thereto prior to the award.

5.2.3 The Contractor shall not contract with any Subcontractor or any person or organization proposed for portions of the Work designated in the bidding requirements or, if none is so designated, with any Subcontractor proposed for the principal portions of the Work who has not been accepted by the Owner and the Architect. The Contractor will not be required to contract with any subcontractor or person or organization against whom he has a reasonable objection.

5.2.4 If the Owner or the Architect requires a change of any proposed Subcontractor or person or organization previously accepted by them, the Contract Sum shall be increased or decreased by the difference in cost occasioned by such change and an appropriate Change Order shall be issued.

5.2.5 The Contractor shall not make any substitution for any Subcontractor or person or organization who has been accepted by the Owner and the Architect, unless the substitution is acceptable to the Owner and the Architect.

5.3 SUBCONTRACTUAL RELATIONS

5.3.1 All work performed for the Contractor by a Subcontractor shall be pursuant to an appropriate agreement between the Contractor and the Subcontractor (and where appropriate between Subcontractors and Sub-subcontractors) which shall contain provisions that:

.1 preserve and protect the rights of the Owner and the Architect under the Contract with respect to the Work to be performed under the subcontract so that the subcontracting thereof will not prejudice such rights;

.2 require that such Work be performed in accordance with the requirements of the Contract Documents;

.3 require submission to the Contractor of applications for payment under each subcontract to which the Contractor is a party, in reasonable time to enable the Contractor to apply for payment in accordance with Article 9;

.4 require that all claims for additional costs, extensions of time, damages for delays or otherwise with respect to subcontracted portions of the Work shall be submitted to the Contractor (via any Subcontractor or Sub-subcontractor where appropriate) in the manner provided in the Contract Documents for like claims by the Contractor upon the Owner;

.5 waive all rights the contracting parties may have against one another for damages caused by fire or other perils covered by the property insurance described in Paragraph 11.3, except such rights as they may have to the proceeds of such insurance held by the Owner as trustee under Paragraph 11.3; and

.6 obligate each Subcontractor specifically to consent to the provisions of this Paragraph 5.3.

5.4 PAYMENTS TO SUBCONTRACTORS

5.4.1 The Contractor shall pay each Subcontractor, upon receipt of payment from the Owner, an amount equal to the percentage of completion allowed to the Contractor on account of such Subcontractor's Work. The Contractor shall also require each Subcontractor to make similar payments to his subcontractors.

5.4.2 If the Architect fails to issue a Certificate for Payment for any cause not the fault of a particular Subcontractor, the Contractor shall pay that Subcontractor on demand, made at any time after the Certificate for Payment should otherwise have been issued, for his Work to the extent completed, less the retained percentage.

5.4.3 The Contractor shall pay each Subcontractor a just share of any insurance moneys received by the Contractor under Article 11, and he shall require each Subcontractor to make similar payments to his subcontractors.

5.4.4 The Architect may, on request and at his discretion, furnish to any Subcontractor, if practicable, information regarding percentages of completion certified to the Contractor on account of Work done by such Subcontractors.

5.4.5 Neither the Owner nor the Architect shall have any obligation to pay or to see to the payment of any moneys to any Subcontractor except as may otherwise be required by law.

ARTICLE 6

SEPARATE CONTRACTS

6.1 OWNER'S RIGHT TO AWARD SEPARATE CONTRACTS

6.1.1 The Owner reserves the right to award other contracts in connection with other portions of the Project under these or similar Conditions of the Contract.

6.1.2 When separate contracts are awarded for different portions of the Project, "the Contractor" in the contract documents in each case shall be the contractor who signs each separate contract.

6.2 MUTUAL RESPONSIBILITY OF CONTRACTORS

6.2.1 The Contractor shall afford other contractors reasonable opportunity for the introduction and storage of their materials and equipment and the execution of their work, and shall properly connect and coordinate his Work with theirs.

6.2.2 If any part of the Contractor's Work depends for proper execution or results upon the work of any other separate contractor, the Contractor shall inspect and promptly report to the Architect any discrepancies or defects in such other work that render it unsuitable for such proper execution and results. Failure of the Contractor so to inspect and report shall constitute an acceptance of the other contractor's work as fit and proper to receive his Work, except as to defects which may develop in the other separate contractor's work after the execution of the Contractor's Work.

6.2.3. Should the Contractor cause damage to the work or property of any separate contractor on the Project, the Contractor shall, upon due notice, settle with such other contractor by agreement or arbitration, if he will so settle. If such separate contractor sues the Owner on account of any damage alleged to have been so sustained, the Owner shall notify the Contractor who shall defend such proceedings and pay all costs in connection therewith, and if any judgment against the Owner' arises therefrom the Contractor shall pay or satisfy it.

6.3 CUTTING AND PATCHING
UNDER SEPARATE CONTRACTS

6.3.1. The Contractor shall do all cutting, fitting or patching of his Work that may be required to fit it to receive or be received by the work of other contractors shown upon, or reasonably implied by, the Contract Documents. The Contractor shall not endanger any work of any other contractors by cutting, excavating or otherwise altering any work and shall not cut or alter the work of any other contractor except with the written consent of the Architect.

6.3.2 Any costs caused by defective or ill-timed work shall be borne by the party responsible therefor.

6.4 OWNER'S RIGHT TO CLEAN UP

6.4.1 If a dispute arises between the separate contractors as to their responsibility for cleaning up as required by Paragraph 4.16, the Owner may clean up and charge the cost thereof to the several contractors as the Architect shall determine to be just.

ARTICLE 7

MISCELLANEOUS PROVISIONS

7.1 LAW OF THE PLACE

7.1.1 The Contract shall be governed by the law of the place where the Project is located.

7.2 SUCCESSORS AND ASSIGNS

7.2.1 The Owner and the Contractor each binds himself, his partners, successors, assigns and legal representatives to the other party hereto and to the partners, successors, assigns and legal representatives of such other party in respect to all covenants, agreements and obligations contained in the Contract Documents. Neither party to the Contract shall assign the Contract or sublet it as a whole without the written consent of the other, nor shall the Contractor assign any moneys due or to become due to him hereunder, without the previous written consent of the Owner.

7.3 WRITTEN NOTICE

7.3.1 Written notice shall be deemed to have been duly served if delivered in person to the individual or member of the firm or to an officer of the corporation for whom it was intended, or if delivered at or sent by registered or certified mail to the last business address known to him who gives the notice.

7.4 CLAIMS FOR DAMAGES

7.4.1 Should either party to the Contract suffer injury or damage to person or property because of any act or omission of the other party or of any of his employees, agents or others for whose acts he is legally liable, claim shall be made in writing to such other party within a reasonable time after the first observance of such injury or damage.

7.5 PERFORMANCE BOND AND
LABOR AND MATERIAL PAYMENT BOND

7.5.1 The Owner shall have the right, prior to signing the Contract, to require the Contractor to furnish bonds covering the faithful performance of the Contract and the payment of all obligations arising thereunder in such form and amount as the Owner may prescribe and with such sureties as may be agreeable to the parties. If such bonds are stipulated in the bidding requirements, the premiums shall be paid by the Contractor; if required subsequent to the submission of quotations or bids, the cost shall be reimbursed by the Owner. The Contractor shall deliver the required bonds to the Owner not later than the date of execution of the Contract, or if the Work is commenced prior thereto in response to a notice to proceed, the Contractor shall, prior to commencement of the Work, submit evidence satisfactory to the Owner that such bonds will be issued.

7.6 OWNER'S RIGHT TO CARRY OUT THE WORK

7.6.1 If the Contractor defaults or neglects to carry out the Work in accordance with the Contract Documents or fails to perform any provision of the Contract, the Owner may, after seven days' written notice to the Contractor and without prejudice to any other remedy he may have, make good such deficiencies. In such case an appropriate Change Order shall be issued deducting from the payments then or thereafter due the Contractor the cost of correcting such deficiencies, including the cost of the Architect's additional services made necessary by such default, neglect or failure. The Architect must approve both such action and the amount charged to the Contractor. If the payments then or thereafter due the Contractor are not sufficient to cover such amount, the Contractor shall pay the difference to the Owner.

7.7 ROYALTIES AND PATENTS

7.7.1 The Contractor shall pay all royalties and license fees. He shall defend all suits or claims for infringement of any patent rights and shall save the Owner harmless from loss on account thereof, except that the Owner shall be responsible for all such loss when a particular design, process or the product of a particular manufacturer or manufacturers is specified, but if the Contractor has reason to believe that the design, process or product specified is an infringement of a patent, he shall be responsible for such loss unless he promptly gives such information to the Architect.

7.8 TESTS

7.8.1 If the Contract Documents, laws, ordinances, rules, regulations or orders of any public authority having jurisdiction require any Work to be inspected, tested or approved, the Contractor shall give the Architect timely notice of its readiness and of the date arranged so the Architect may observe such inspection, testing or approval. The Contractor shall bear all costs of such inspections, tests and approvals unless otherwise provided.

7.8.2 If after the commencement of the Work the Architect determines that any Work requires special inspection, testing or approval which Subparagraph 7.8.1 does not include, he will, upon written authorization from the Owner, instruct the Contractor to order such special inspection, testing or approval, and the Contractor shall give notice as in Subparagraph 7.8.1. If such special inspection or testing reveals a failure of the Work to comply with the requirements of the Contract Documents, laws, ordinances, rules, regulations or orders of any public authority having jurisdiction, the Contractor shall bear all costs thereof, including the Architect's additional services made necessary by such failure; otherwise the Owner shall bear such costs, and an appropriate Change Order shall be issued.

7.8.3. Required certificates of inspection, testing or approval shall be secured by the Contractor and promptly delivered by him to the Architect.

7.8.4 If the Architect wishes to observe the inspections, tests or approvals required by this Paragraph 7.8, he will do so promptly and, where practicable, at the source of supply.

7.8.5 Neither the observations of the Architect in his administration of the Contract, nor inspections, tests or approvals by persons other than the Contractor shall relieve the Contractor from his obligations to perform the Work in accordance with the Contract Documents.

7.9 INTEREST

7.9.1 Any moneys not paid when due under this Contract shall bear interest at the legal rate in force at the place of the Project.

7.10 ARBITRATION

7.10.1 All claims, disputes and other matters in question arising out of, or relating to, this Contract or the breach thereof, except as set forth in Subparagraph 2.2.9 with respect to the Architect's decisions on matters relating to artistic effect, and except for claims which have been waived by the making or acceptance of final payment as provided by Subparagraphs 9.7.5 and 9.7.6, shall be decided by arbitration in accordance with the Construction Industry Arbitration Rules of the American Arbitration Association then obtaining. This agreement so to arbitrate shall be specifically enforceable under the prevailing arbitration law. The award rendered by the arbitrators shall be final, and judgment may be entered upon it in any court having jurisdiction thereof.

7.10.2 Notice of the demand for arbitration shall be filed in writing with the other party to the Contract and with the American Arbitration Association, and a copy shall be filed with the Architect. The demand for arbitration shall be made within the time limits specified in Subparagraphs 2.2.10 and 2.2.11 where applicable, and in all other cases within a reasonable time after the claim, dispute or other matter in question has arisen, and in no event shall it be made after institution of legal or equitable proceedings based on such claim, dispute or other matter in question would be barred by the applicable statute of limitations.

7.10.3 The Contractor shall carry on the Work and maintain the progress schedule during any arbitration proceedings, unless otherwise agreed by him and the Owner in writing.

ARTICLE 8

TIME

8.1 DEFINITIONS

8.1.1 The Contract Time is the period of time allotted in the Contract Documents for completion of the Work.

8.1.2 The date of commencement of the Work is the date established in a notice to proceed. If there is no notice to proceed, it shall be the date of the Agreement or such other date as may be established therein.

8.1.3 The Date of Substantial Completion of the Work or designated portion thereof is the Date certified by the Architect when construction is sufficiently complete, in accordance with the Contract Documents, so the Owner may occupy the Work or designated portion thereof for the use for which it is intended.

8.2 PROGRESS AND COMPLETION

8.2.1. All time limits stated in the Contract Documents are of the essence of the Contract.

8.2.2 The Contractor shall begin the Work on the date of commencement as defined in Subparagraph 8.1.2. He shall carry the Work forward expeditiously with adequate forces and shall complete it within the Contract Time.

8.3 DELAYS AND EXTENSIONS OF TIME

8.3.1 If the Contractor is delayed at any time in the progress of the Work by any act or neglect of the Owner or the Architect, or by any employee of either, or by any separate contractor employed by the Owner, or by changes ordered in the Work, or by labor disputes, fire, unusual delay in transportation, unavoidable casualties or any causes beyond the Contractor's control, or by delay authorized by the Owner pending arbitration, or by any cause which the Architect determines may justify the delay, then the Contract Time shall be extended by Change Order for such reasonable time as the Architect may determine.

8.3.2. All claims for extension of time shall be made in writing to the Architect no more than fifteen days after the occurrence of the delay; otherwise they shall be waived.

8.3.3 If no schedule or agreement is made stating the dates upon which written interpretations as set forth in Subparagraph 1.2.5 shall be furnished, then no claim for delay shall be allowed on account of failure to furnish such interpretations until fifteen days after demand is made for them, and not then unless such claim is reasonable.

8.3.4 This Paragraph 8.3 does not exclude the recovery of damages for delay by either party under other provisions of the Contract Documents.

ARTICLE 9

PAYMENTS AND COMPLETION

9.1 CONTRACT SUM

9.1.1 The Contract Sum is stated in the Agreement and is the total amount payable by the Owner to the Contractor for the performance of the Work under the Contract Documents.

9.2 SCHEDULE OF VALUES

9.2.1 Before the first Application for Payment, the Contractor shall submit to the Architect a schedule of values of the various portions of the Work, including quantities if required by the Architect, aggregating the total Contract Sum, divided so as to facilitate payments to Subcontractors in accordance with Paragraph 5.4, prepared in such form as specified or as the Architect and the Contractor may agree upon, and supported by such data to substantiate its correctness as the Architect may require. Each item in the schedule of values shall include its proper share of overhead, profit, and other general charges. This schedule, when approved by the Architect, shall be used as a basis for the Contractor's Applications for Payment.

9.3 PROGRESS PAYMENTS

9.3.1 At least ten days before each progress payment falls due, the Contractor shall submit to the Architect an itemized Application for Payment, supported by such data substantiating the Contractor's right to payment as the Owner or the Architect may require.

9.3.2 If payments are to be made on account of materials or equipment not incorporated in the Work but delivered and suitably stored at the site, or at some other location agreed upon in writing, such payments shall be conditioned upon submission by the Contractor of bills of sale or such other procedures satisfactory to the Owner to establish the Owner's title to such materials or equipment or otherwise protect the Owner's interest including applicable insurance and transportation to the site.

9.3.3 The Contractor warrants and guarantees that title to all Work, materials and equipment covered by an Application for Payment, whether incorporated in the Project or not, will have passed to the Owner prior to the making of the Application for Payment, free and clear of all liens, claims, security interests or encumbrances, hereinafter referred to in this Article 9 as "liens"; and that no Work, materials or equipment covered by an Application for Payment will have been acquired by the Contractor, or by any other person performing the Work at the site or furnishing materials and equipment for the Project, subject to an agreement under which an interest therein or an encumbrance thereon is retained by the seller or otherwise imposed by the Contractor or such other person.

9.4 CERTIFICATES FOR PAYMENT

9.4.1 If the Contractor has made Application for Payment as above, the Architect will, with reasonable promptness but not more than seven days after the receipt of the Application, issue a Certificate for Payment to the Owner for such amount as he determines to be properly due, or state in writing his reasons for withholding a Certificate as provided in Subparagraph 9.5.1.

9.4.2 The issuance of a Certificate for Payment will constitute a representation by the Architect to the Owner, based on his observations at the site as provided in Subparagraph 2.2.4 and the data comprising the Application for Payment, that the Work has progressed to the point indicated; that, to the best of his knowledge, information and belief, the quality of the Work is in accordance with the Contract Documents (subject to an evaluation of the Work as a functioning whole upon Substantial Completion, to the results of any subsequent tests required by the Contract Documents, to minor deviations from the Contract Documents correctable prior to completion, and to any specific qualifications stated in his Certificate); and that the Contractor is entitled to payment in the amount certified. In addition, the Architect's final Certificate for Payment will constitute a further representation that the conditions precedent to the Contractor's being entitled to final payment as set forth in Subparagraph 9.7.2 have been fulfilled. However, by issuing a Certificate for Payment, the Architect shall not thereby be deemed to represent that he has made exhaustive or continuous on-site inspections to check the quality or quantity of the Work or that he has reviewed the construction means, methods, techniques, sequences or procedures, or that he has made any examination to ascertain how or for what purpose the Contractor has used the moneys previously paid on account of the Contract Sum.

9.4.3 After the Architect has issued a Certificate for Payment, the Owner shall make payment in the manner provided in the Agreement.

9.4.4 No Certificate for a progress payment, nor any progress payment, nor any partial or entire use or occupancy of the Project by the Owner, shall consitute an acceptance of any Work not in accordance with the Contract Documents.

9.5 PAYMENTS WITHHELD

9.5.1 The Architect may decline to approve an Application for Payment and may withhold his Certificate in whole or in part if in his opinion he is unable to make representations to the Owner as provided in Subparagraph 9.4.2. The Architect may also decline to approve any Applications for Payment or, because of subsequently discovered evidence or subsequent inspections, he may nullify the whole or any part of any Certificate for Payment previously issued to such extent as may be necessary in his opinion to protect the Owner from loss because of:

   .1 defective work not remedied,
   .2 claims filed or reasonable evidence indicating probable filing of claims,
   .3 failure of the Contractor to make payments properly to Subcontractors or for labor, materials or equipment,
   .4 reasonable doubt that the Work can be completed for the unpaid balance of the Contract Sum,
   .5 damage to another contractor,
   .6 reasonable indication that the Work will not be completed within the Contract Time, or
   .7 unsatisfactory prosecution of the Work by the Contractor.

9.5.2 When the above grounds in Subparagraph 9.5.1 are removed, payment shall be made for amounts withheld because of them.

9.6 FAILURE OF PAYMENT

9.6.1 If the Architect should fail to issue any Certificate for Payment, through no fault of the Contractor, within seven days after receipt of the Contractor's Application for Payment, or if the Owner should fail to pay the Contractor within seven days after the date of payment established in the Agreement any amount certified by the Architect or awarded by arbitration, then the Contractor may, upon seven additional days' written notice to the Owner and the Architect, stop the Work until payment of the amount owing has been received.

9.7 SUBSTANTIAL COMPLETION AND FINAL PAYMENT

9.7.1 When the Contractor determines that the Work or a designated portion thereof acceptable to the Owner is substantially complete, the Contractor shall prepare for submission to the Architect a list of items to be completed or corrected. The failure to include any items on such list does not alter the responsibility of the Contractor to complete all Work in accordance with the Contract Documents. When the Architect on the basis of an inspection determines that the Work is substantially complete, he will then prepare a Certificate of Substantial Completion, which shall establish the Date of Substantial Completion, shall state the responsibilities of the Owner and the Contractor for maintenance, heat, utilities, and insurance, and shall fix the time within which the Contractor shall complete the items listed therein, said time to be within the Contract Time. The Certificate of Substantial Completion shall be submitted to the Owner and the Contractor for their written acceptance of the responsibilities assigned to them in such Certificate.

9.7.2. Upon receipt of written notice that the Work is ready for final inspection and acceptance and upon receipt of a final Application for Payment, the Architect will promptly make such inspection and, when he finds the Work acceptable under the Contract Documents and the Contract fully performed, he will promptly issue a final Certificate for Payment stating that to the best of his knowledge, information and belief, and on the basis of his observations and inspections, the Work has been completed in accordance with the terms and conditions of the Contract Documents and that the entire balance found to be due the Contractor, and noted in said final Certificate, is due and payable.

9.7.3 Neither the final payment nor any part of the retained percentage shall become due until the Contractor submits to the Architect: releases or waivers of all liens arising out of the Contract; an Affidavit that the releases and waivers include all the labor, materials and equipment for which a lien could be filed and that all payrolls, bills for materials and equipment, and other indebtedness connected with the Work for which the Owner or his property might in any way be responsible have been paid or otherwise satisfied; consent of surety, if any, to final payment; and such other data establishing payment or satisfaction of all such obligations as the Owner may require. If any Subcontractor refuses to furnish a release or waiver, the Contractor may furnish a bond satisfactory to the Owner to indemnify him against any such lien. If any such lien remains unsatisfied after all payments are made, the Contractor shall refund to the Owner all moneys that the latter may be compelled to pay in discharging such lien, including all costs and reasonable attorneys' fees.

9.7.4 If after Substantial Completion of the Work final completion thereof is materially delayed through no fault of the Contractor, and the Architect so confirms, the Owner shall, upon certification by the Architect, and without terminating the Contract, make payment of the balance due for that portion of the Work fully completed and accepted. If the remaining balance for Work not fully completed or corrected is less than the retainage stipulated in the Agreement, and if bonds have been furnished as required in Subparagraph 7.5.1, the written consent of the surety to the payment of the balance due for that portion of the Work fully completed and accepted shall be submitted by the Contractor to the Architect prior to certification of such payment. Such payment shall be

made under the terms and conditions governing final payment, except that it shall not constitute a waiver of claims.

9.7.5 The making of final payment shall constitute a waiver of all claims by the Owner except those arising from:

    .1 unsettled liens,

    .2 faulty or defective Work appearing after Substantial Completion,

    .3 failure of the Work to comply with the requirements of the Contract Documents,

    .4 terms of any special guarantees required by the Contract Documents.

9.7.6 The acceptance of final payment shall constitute a waiver of all claims by the Contractor except those previously made in writing and still unsettled.

ARTICLE 10

PROTECTION OF PERSONS AND PROPERTY

10.1 SAFETY PRECAUTIONS AND PROGRAMS

10.1.1 The Contractor shall be responsible for initiating, maintaining and supervising all safety precautions and programs in connection with the Work.

10.2 SAFETY OF PERSONS AND PROPERTY

10.2.1 The Contractor shall take all necessary precautions for the safety of, and shall provide all necessary protection to prevent damage, injury or loss to:

    .1 all employees on the Work and all other persons who may be affected thereby.

    .2 all the Work and all materials and equipment to be incorporated therein, whether in storage on or off the site, and

    .3 other property at the site or adjacent thereto, including trees, shrubs, lawns, walks, pavements, roadways, structures and utilities not designated for removal, relocation or replacement in the course of construction.

10.2.2 The Contractor shall comply with all applicable laws, ordinances, rules, regulations and orders of any public authority having jurisdiction for the safety of persons or property or to protect them from damage, injury or loss. He shall erect and maintain, as required by existing conditions and progress of the Work, all necessary safeguards for safety and protection, including posting danger signs and other warnings against hazards, promulgating safety regulations and notifying owners and users of adjacent utilities.

10.2.3 When the use or storage of explosives or other hazardous materials or equipment is necessary for the execution of the Work, the Contractor shall exercise the utmost care and shall carry on such activities under the supervision of properly qualified personnel.

10.2.4 All damage or loss to any property referred to in Clauses 10.2.1.2 and 10.2.1.3 caused in whole or in part by the Contractor, any Subcontractor, any Sub-subcontractor, or anyone directly or indirectly employed by any of them, or by anyone for whose acts any of them may be liable, shall be remedied by the Contractor, except damage or loss attributable to faulty Drawings or Specifications or to the acts or omissions of the Owner or Architect or anyone employed by either of them or for whose acts either of them may be liable, and not attributable to the fault or negligence of the Contractor.

10.2.5 The Contractor shall designate a responsible member of his organization at the site whose duty shall be the prevention of accidents. This person shall be the Contractor's superintendent unless otherwise designated in writing by the Contractor to the Owner and the Architect.

10.2.6 The Contractor shall not load or permit any part of the Work to be loaded so as to endanger its safety.

10.3 EMERGENCIES

10.3.1 In any emergency affecting the safety of persons or property, the Contractor shall act, at his discretion, to prevent threatened damage, injury or loss. Any additional compensation or extension of time claimed by the Contractor on account of emergency work shall be determined as provided in Article 12 for Changes in the Work.

ARTICLE 11

INSURANCE

11.1 CONTRACTOR'S LIABILITY INSURANCE

11.1.1 The Contractor shall purchase and maintain such insurance as will protect him from claims set forth below which may arise out of or result from the Contractor's operations under the Contract, whether such operations be by himself or by any Subcontractor or by anyone directly or indirectly employed by any of them, or by anyone for whose acts any of them may be liable:

> .1 claims under workmen's compensation, disability benefit and other similar employee benefit acts;
>
> .2 claims for damages because of bodily injury, occupational sickness or disease, or death of his employees, and claims insured by usual personal injury liability coverage;
>
> .3 claims for damages because of bodily injury, sickness or disease, or death of any person other than his employees, and claims insured by usual personal injury liability coverage; and
>
> .4 claims for damages because of injury to or destruction of tangible property, including loss of use resulting therefrom.

11.1.2. The insurance required by Subparagraph 11.1.1 shall be written for not less than any limits of liability specified in the Contract Documents, or required by law, whichever is greater, and shall include contractual liability insurance as applicable to the Contractor's obligations under Paragraph 4.18.

11.1.3 Certificates of Insurance acceptable to the Owner shall be filed with the Owner prior to commencement of the Work. These Certificates shall contain a provision that coverages afforded under the policies will not be cancelled until at least fifteen days' prior written notice has been given to the Owner.

11.2 OWNER'S LIABILITY INSURANCE

11.2.1 The Owner shall be responsible for purchasing and maintaining his own liability insurance and, at his option, may purchase and maintain such insurance as will protect him against claims which may arise from operations under the Contract.

11.3 PROPERTY INSURANCE

11.3.1 Unless otherwise provided, the Owner shall purchase and maintain property insurance upon the entire Work at the site to the full insurable value thereof. This insurance shall include the interests of the Owner, the Contractor, Subcontractors and Sub-subcontractors in the Work and shall insure against the perils of Fire, Extended Coverage, Vandalism and Malicious Mischief.

11.3.2 The Owner shall purchase and maintain such steam boiler and machinery insurance as may be required by the Contract Documents or by law. This insurance shall include the interests of the Owner, the Contractor, Subcontractors and Sub-subcontractors in the Work.

11.3.3 Any insured loss is to be adjusted with the Owner and made payable to the Owner as trustee for the insureds, as their interests may appear, subject to the requirements of any applicable mortgagee clause and of Subparagraph 11.3.8.

11.3.4 The Owner shall file a copy of all policies with the Contractor before an exposure to loss may occur. If the Owner does not intend to purchase such insurance, he shall inform the Contractor in writing prior to commencement of the Work. The Contractor may then effect insurance which will protect the interests of himself, his Subcontractors and the Sub-subcontractors in the Work, and by appropriate Change Order the cost thereof shall be charged to the Owner. If the Contractor is damaged by failure of the Owner to purchase or maintain such insurance and so to notify the Contractor, then the Owner shall bear all reasonable costs properly attributable thereto.

11.3.5 If the Contractor requests in writing that other special insurance be included in the property insurance policy, the Owner shall, if possible, include such insurance, and the cost thereof shall be charged to the Contractor by appropriate Change Order.

11.3.6 The Owner and Contractor waive all rights against each other for damages caused by fire or other perils to the extent covered by insurance provided under this Paragraph 11.3, except such rights as they may have to the proceeds of such insurance held by the Owner as trustee. The Contractor shall require similar waivers by Subcontractors and Sub-subcontractors in accordance with Clause 5.3.1.5.

11.3.7 If required in writing by any party in interest, the Owner as trustee shall, upon the occurrence of an insured loss, give bond for the proper performance of his duties. He shall deposit in a separate account any money so received, and he shall distribute it in accordance with such agreement as the parties in interest may reach, or in accordance with an award by arbitration in which case the procedure shall be as provided in Paragraph 7.10. If after such loss no other special agreement is made, replacement of damaged work shall be covered by an appropriate Change Order.

11.3.8. The Owner as trustee shall have power to adjust and settle any loss with the insurers unless one of the parties in interest shall object in writing within five days after the occurrence of loss to the Owner's exercise of this power, and if such objection be made, arbitrators shall be chosen as provided in Paragraph 7.10. The Owner as trustee shall, in that case, make settlement with the insurers in accordance with the directions of such arbitrators. If distribution of the insurance proceeds by arbitration is required, the arbitrators will direct such distribution.

11.4 LOSS OF USE INSURANCE

11.4.1 The Owner, at his option, may purchase and maintain such insurance as will insure him against loss of use of his property due to fire or other hazards, however caused.

ARTICLE 12

CHANGES IN THE WORK

12.1 CHANGE ORDERS

12.1.1 The Owner, without invalidating the Contract, may order Changes in the Work consisting of additions, deletions or other revisions, the Contract Sum and the Contract Time being adjusted accordingly. All such Changes in the Work shall be authorized by Change Order, and shall be executed under the applicable conditions of the Contract Documents.

12.1.2 A Change Order is a written order to the Contractor signed by the Owner and the Architect, issued after the execution of the Contract, authorizing a Change in the Work or an adjustment in the Contract Sum or the Contract Time. Alternatively, the Change Order may be signed by the Architect alone, provided he has written authority from the Owner for such procedure. The Contract Sum and the Contract Time may be changed only by Change Order.

12.1.3 The cost or credit to the Owner resulting from a Change in the Work shall be determined in one or more of the following ways:

  .1 by mutual acceptance of a lump sum properly itemized;

  .2 by unit prices stated in the Contract Documents or subsequently agreed upon; or

  .3 by cost and a mutually acceptable fixed or percentage fee.

12.1.4 If none of the methods set forth in Subparagraph 12.1.3 is agreed upon, the Contractor, provided he receives a Change Order, shall promptly proceed with the Work involved. The cost of such Work shall then be determined by the Architect on the basis of the Contractor's reasonable expenditures and savings, including, in the case of an increase in the Contract Sum, a reasonable allowance for overhead and profit. In such case, and also under Clause 12.1.3.3 above, the Contractor shall keep and present, in such form as the Architect may prescribe, an itemized accounting together with appropriate supporting data. Pending final determination of cost to the Owner, payments on account shall be made on the Architect's Certificate for Payment. The amount of credit to be allowed by the Contractor to the Owner for any deletion or change which results in a net decrease in cost will be the amount of the actual net decrease as confirmed by the Architect. When both additions and credits are involved in any one change, the allowance for overhead and profit shall be figured on the basis of net increase, if any.

12.1.5. If unit prices are stated in the Contract Documents or subsequently agreed upon, and if the quantities originally contemplated are so changed in a proposed Change Order that application of the agreed unit prices to the quantities of Work proposed will create a hardship on the Owner or the Contractor, the applicable unit prices shall be equitably adjusted to prevent such hardship.

12.1.6 Should conditions encountered below the surface of the ground be at variance with the conditions indicated by the Contract Documents, the Contract Sum shall be equitably adjusted by Change Order upon claim by either party made within a reasonable time after the first observance of the conditions.

12.1.7 If the Contractor claims that additional cost or time is involved because of **(1)** any written interpretation issued pursuant to Subparagraph 1.2.5, **(2)** any order by the Architect to stop the Work pursuant to Subparagraph 2.2.12 where the Contractor was not at fault, or **(3)** any written order for a minor change in the Work issued pursuant to Paragraph 12.3, the Contractor shall make such claim as provided in Paragraph 12.2.

12.2 CLAIMS FOR ADDITIONAL COST OR TIME

12.2.1 If the Contractor wishes to make a claim for an increase in the Contract Sum or an extension in the Contract Time, he shall give the Architect written notice thereof within a reasonable time after the occurrence of the event giving rise to such claim. This notice shall be given by the Contractor before proceeding to execute the Work, except in an emergency endangering life or property in which case the Contractor shall proceed in accordance with Subparagraph 10.3.1. No such claim shall be valid unless so made. If the Owner and the Contractor cannot agree on the amount of the adjustment in the Contract Sum or the Contract Time, it shall be determined by the Architect. Any change in the Contract Sum or Contract Time resulting from such claim shall be authorized by Change Order.

12.3 MINOR CHANGES IN THE WORK

12.3.1 The Architect shall have authority to order minor changes in the Work not involving an adjustment in the Contract Sum or an extension of the Contract Time and not inconsistent with the intent of the Contract Documents. Such changes may be effected by Field Order or by other written order. Such changes shall be binding on the Owner and the Contractor.

12.4 FIELD ORDERS

12.4.1 The Architect may issue written Field Orders which interpret the Contract Documents in accordance with Subparagraph 1.2.5 or which order minor changes in the Work in accordance with Paragraph 12.3 without change in Contract Sum or Contract Time. The Contractor shall carry out such Field Orders promptly.

ARTICLE 13

UNCOVERING AND CORRECTION OF WORK

13.1 UNCOVERING OF WORK

13.1.1 If any Work should be covered contrary to the request of the Architect, it must, if required by the Architect, be uncovered for his observation and replaced, at the Contractor's expense.

13.1.2 If any other Work has been covered which the Architect has not specifically requested to observe prior to being covered, the Architect may request to see such Work and it shall be uncovered by the Contractor. If such Work be found in accordance with the Contract Documents, the cost of uncovering and replacement shall, by appropriate Change Order, be charged to the Owner. If such Work be found not in accordance with the Contract Documents, the Contractor shall pay such costs unless it be found that this condition was caused by a separate contractor employed as provided in Article 6, and in that event the Owner shall be responsible for the payment of such costs.

13.2 CORRECTION OF WORK

13.2.1 The Contractor shall promptly correct all Work rejected by the Architect as defective or as failing to conform to the Contract Documents whether observed before or after Substantial Completion and whether or not fabricated, installed or completed. The Contractor shall bear all costs of correcting such rejected Work, including the cost of the Architect's additional services thereby made necessary.

13.2.2 If, within one year after the Date of Substantial Completion or within such longer period of time as may be prescribed by law or by the terms of any applicable special guarantee required by the Contract Documents, any of the Work is found to be defective or not in accordance with the Contract Documents, the Contractor shall correct it promptly after receipt of a written notice from the Owner to do so unless the Owner has previously given the Contractor a written acceptance of such condition. The Owner shall give such notice promptly after discovery of the condition.

13.2.3 All such defective or non-conforming Work under Subparagraphs 13.2.1 and 13.2.2 shall be removed from the site where necessary, and the Work shall be corrected to comply with the Contract Documents without cost to the Owner.

13.2.4 The Contractor shall bear the cost of making good all work of separate contractors destroyed or damaged by such removal or correction.

13.2.5 If the Contractor does not remove such defective or non-conforming Work within a reasonable time fixed by written notice from the Architect, the Owner may remove it and may store the materials or equipment at the expense of the Contractor. If the Contractor does not pay the cost of such removal and storage within ten days thereafter, the Owner may upon ten additional days' written notice sell such Work at auction or at private sale and shall account for the net proceeds thereof, after deducting all the costs that should have been borne by the Contractor including compensation for additional architectural services. If such proceeds of sale do not cover all costs which the Contractor should have borne, the difference shall be charged to the Contractor and an appropriate Change Order shall be issued. If the payments then or thereafter due the Contractor are not sufficient to cover such amount, the Contractor shall pay the difference to the Owner.

13.2.6 If the Contractor fails to correct such defective or non-conforming Work, the Owner may correct it in accordance with Paragraph 7.6.

13.2.7 The obligations of the Contractor under this Paragraph 13.2 shall be in addition to and not in limitation of any obligations imposed upon him by special guarantees required by the Contract Documents or otherwise prescribed by law.

13.3 ACCEPTANCE OF DEFECTIVE OR NON-CONFORMING WORK

13.3.1 If the Owner prefers to accept defective or non-conforming Work, he may do so instead of requiring its removal and correction, in which case a Change Order will be issued to reflect an appropriate reduction in the Contract Sum, or, if the amount is determined after final payment, it shall be paid by the Contractor.

ARTICLE 14

TERMINATION OF THE CONTRACT

14.1 TERMINATION BY THE CONTRACTOR

14.1.1 If the Work is stopped for a period of thirty days under an order of any court or other public authority having jurisdiction, through no act or fault of the Contractor or a Subcontractor or their agents or employees or any other persons performing any of the Work under a contract with the Contractor, or if the Work should be stopped for a period of thirty days by the Contractor for the Architect's failure to issue a Certificate for Payment as provided in Paragraph 9.6 or for the Owner's failure to make payment thereon as provided in Paragraph 9.6, then the Contractor may, upon seven days' written notice to the Owner and the Architect, terminate the Contract and recover from the Owner payment for all Work executed and for any proven loss sustained upon any materials, equipment, tools, construction equipment and machinery, including reasonable profit and damages.

14.2 TERMINATION BY THE OWNER

14.2.1 If the Contractor is adjudged a bankrupt, or if he makes a general assignment for the benefit of his creditors, or if a receiver is appointed on account of his insolvency, or if he persistently or repeatedly refuses or fails, except in cases for which extension of time is provided, to supply enough properly skilled workmen or proper materials, or if he fails to make prompt payment to Subcontractors or for materials or labor, or persistently disregards laws, ordinances, rules, regulations or orders of any public authority having jurisdiction, or otherwise is guilty of a substantial violation of a provision of the Contract Documents, then the Owner, upon certification by the Architect that sufficient cause exists to justify such action, may, without prejudice to any right or remedy and after giving the Contractor and his surety, if any, seven days' written notice, terminate the employment of the Contractor and take possession of the site and of all materials, equipment, tools, construction equipment and machinery thereon owned by the Contractor and may finish the Work by whatever method he may deem expedient. In such case the Contractor shall not be entitled to receive any further payment until the Work is finished.

14.2.2 If the unpaid balance of the Contract Sum exceeds the costs of finishing the Work, including compensation for the Architect's additional services, such excess shall be paid to the Contractor. If such costs exceed such unpaid balance, the Contractor shall pay the difference to the Owner. The costs incurred by the Owner as herein provided shall be certified by the Architect.

THE AMERICAN INSTITUTE OF ARCHITECTS

INSTRUCTIONS ON THE USE OF APRIL 1967 SUPPLEMENT TO

AIA Document A201

General Conditions of the Contract for Construction

1. The AIA/AGC Liaison Commission met in special session on Monday, 10 April 1967 to discuss and resolve objections held by AGC to various provisions of AIA Document A201. Those in attendance included the regular members of the AIA/AGC Liaison Commission, Robert L. Durham, FAIA, First Vice President of AIA, Fred W. Mast, Senior Vice President of AGC, several members of the AIA Committee on Documents Review and the AGC Contracts Committee, legal and insurance counsels and staff of both organizations.

2. This special session was convened to put an end to misunderstandings still being experienced in some localities which were delaying certain projects and to stop contractors' requests to continue use of the 1963 edition of A201.

3. Although many architects in many areas were experiencing no difficulties with the 1966 document, the AIA representatives deemed it wise to consider modifications that would create nationwide harmony in the construction industry.

4. A list of proposed changes in the document was reduced to modifications of wording in seventeen subparagraphs which architects and contractors agreed should be clarified. The accepted modifications achieve the desired clarification for contractors without changing the intent of the 1966 document as originally written to deal adequately with current problems of architectural practice.

5. These modifications implement the general principles agreed to by AIA and AGC at their 10 January 1967 meeting that the architect is responsible for his professional services and that the contractor is responsible for construction operations and safety procedures until final completion.

6. The modified Subparagraphs attached are to be substituted for the present wording in the September 1966 edition of A201 by Addendum, Supplementary Conditions, Change Order or other appropriate means. The SUPPLEMENTAL SHEET is also designed to be bound into the Specifications, Project Manual, etc., with appropriate instructions in the Supplementary Conditions.

7. Until the next regular printing of A201 containing the modified Subparagraphs is available, and, the present stock is depleted, this INSTRUCTION AND SUPPLEMENT sheet will be furnished with all orders for A201. Due to the great number of A201 documents now in circulation, it is physically impossible to replace these with a completely revised document. *Please do not return your present document stock because no replacements containing these modifications are available.*

8. There have been some reports that AGC has rejected the recent modification to Paragraph 4.18. These reports are erroneous and should be disregarded. AGC has adopted and approved the modification to Subparagraph 4.18.3. Insurance is generally available and companies have prepared required forms and established rates for coverage.

9. The use of the September 1966 Edition of A201 by all architects is again strongly urged by the Institute. The 1963 Edition of A201 is totally inadequate in its protection of the parties to the present-day liability climate. The AIA/AGC Liaison Commission agreed that the September 1966 Edition of A201 as modified should be used by architects and contractors immediately.

10. Any architect encountering any further local objections to A201 as modified should report this immediately to AIA Headquarters.

11. Documents Information Bulletin #5, dated 19 April 1967, was mailed to all Chapter & State Presidents, all Chapter & State Executives and Secretaries and AIA Board of Directors. This Bulletin listed the new wording and deleted or modified wording of the Subparagraphs. Members desiring to see this Bulletin should contact their local chapter office or president.

12. PERMISSION IS GRANTED BY THE AIA TO REPRODUCE THIS INSTRUCTION AND SUPPLEMENT SHEET.

INSTRUCTIONS FOR APRIL 1967 SUPPLEMENT TO **AIA DOCUMENT A 201**, SEPT. 1966 EDITION
THE AMERICAN INSTITUTE OF ARCHITECTS, 1735 N.Y. AVE., N.W., WASHINGTON, D.C. 20006
AIA DOCUMENT A 201 • GENERAL CONDITIONS OF THE CONTRACT FOR CONSTRUCTION • TENTH EDITION • AIA®
SEPTEMBER 1966 © THE AMERICAN INSTITUTE OF ARCHITECTS, 1735 NEW YORK AVENUE, N.W., WASHINGTON, D.C. 20006

APRIL 1967 SUPPLEMENT • SUBPARAGRAPHS 1.2.3, 4.5.1, 4.5.2, 4.7.2, 4.8.1, 4.9.1, 5.2.2,
5.4.2, 6.2.3, 7.8.2, 7.10.1, 9.3.3, 9.7.1, 10.2.1, 10.2.2, 11.3.4, AND 12.1.6 REVISED

1.2 EXECUTION, CORRELATION, INTENT AND INTERPRETATIONS

1.2.3 The Contract Documents are complementary, and what is required by any one shall be as binding as if required by all. The intention of the Documents is to include all labor, materials, equipment and other items as provided in Subparagraph 4.4.1 necessary for the proper execution and completion of the Work, and also to include all work which may be reasonably inferable from the Contract Documents as being necessary to produce the intended results. Words which have well-known technical or trade meanings are used herein in accordance with such recognized meanings.

4.5 WARRANTY

4.5.1 The Contractor warrants to the Owner and the Architect that all materials and equipment incorporated in the Project will be new unless otherwise specified, and that all Work will be of good quality, free from faults and defects and in conformance with the Contract Documents. All Work not so conforming to these standards may be considered defective. If required by the Architect, the Contractor shall furnish satisfactory evidence as to the kind and quality of materials and equipment.

4.5.2 The warranty provided in this Paragraph 4.5 shall be in addition to and not in limitation of any other warranty or remedy required by law or by the Contract Documents.

4.7 PERMITS, FEES AND NOTICES

4.7.2 The Contractor shall give all notices and comply with all laws, ordinances, rules, regulations and orders of any public authority bearing on the performance of the Work. If the Contractor observes that any of the Contract Documents are at variance therewith in any respect, he shall promptly notify the Architect in writing, and any necessary changes shall be adjusted by appropriate Modification. If the Contractor performs any Work knowing it to be contrary to such laws, ordinances, rules and regulations, and without such notice to the Architect, he shall assume full responsibility therefor and shall bear all costs attributable thereto.

4.8 CASH ALLOWANCES

4.8.1 The Contractor shall include in the Contract Sum all allowances stated in the Contract Documents. These allowances shall cover the net cost of the materials and equipment delivered and unloaded at the site, and all applicable taxes. The Contractor's handling costs on the site, labor, installation costs, overhead, profit and other expenses contemplated for the original allowance shall be included in the Contract Sum and not in the allowance. The Contractor shall cause the Work covered by these allowances to be performed for such amounts and by such persons as the Architect may direct, but he will not be required to employ persons against whom he makes a reasonable objection. If the cost, when determined, is more than or less than the allowance, the Contract Sum shall be adjusted accordingly by Change Order which will include additional handling costs on the site, labor, installation costs, overhead profit and other ex-

penses resulting to the Contractor from any increase over the original allowance.

4.9 SUPERINTENDENT

4.9.1 The Contractor shall employ a competent superintendent and necessary assistants who shall be in attendance at the Project site during the progress of the Work. The superintendent shall be satisfactory to the Architect, and shall not be changed except with the consent of the Architect, unless the superintendent proves to be unsatisfactory to the Contractor and ceases to be in his employ. The superintendent shall represent the Contractor and all communications given to the superintendent shall be as binding as if given to the Contractor. Important communications will be confirmed in writing. Other communications will be so confirmed on written request in each case.

5.2 AWARD OF SUBCONTRACTS AND OTHER CONTRACTS FOR PORTIONS OF THE WORK

5.2.2 If, prior to the award of the Contract, the Owner or Architect has a reasonable and substantial objection to any person or organization on such list, and refuses in writing to accept such person or organization, the sucessful bidder may, prior to the award, withdraw his bid without forfeiture of bid security. If the successful bidder submits an acceptable substitute with an increase in his bid price to cover the difference in cost occasioned by such substitution, the Owner may, at his discretion, accept the increased bid price or he may disqualify the bid. If, after the award, the Owner or Architect refuses to accept any person or organization on such list, the Contractor shall submit an acceptable substitute and the Contract Sum shall be increased or decreased by the difference in cost occasioned by such substitution and an appropriate Change Order shall be issued; however, no increase in the Contract Sum shall be allowed for any such substitution unless the Contractor has acted promptly and responsively in submitting a name with respect thereto prior to the award.

5.4 PAYMENTS TO SUBCONTRACTORS

5.4.2 If the Architect fails to issue a Certificate for Payment for any cause which is the fault of the Contractor and not the fault of a particular Subcontractor, the Contractor shall pay that Subcontractor on demand, made at any time after the Certificate for Payment should otherwise have been issued, for his Work to the extent completed, less the retained percentage.

6.2 MUTUAL RESPONSIBILITY OF CONTRACTORS

6.2.3 Should the Contractor cause damage to the work or property of any separate contractor on the Project, the Contractor shall, upon due notice, settle with such other contractor by agreement or arbitration, if he will so settle. If such separate contractor sues the Owner on account of any damage alleged to have been so sustained, the Owner shall notify the Contractor who shall defend such proceedings at the Owner's expense and, if any judgment against the Owner arises therefrom, the Contractor shall pay or satisfy it and shall reimburse the

Owner for all attorneys' fees and court costs which the Owner has incurred.

7.8 TESTS

7.8.2 If after the commencement of the Work the Architect determines that any Work requires special inspection, testing or approval which Subparagraph 7.8.1 does not include, he will, upon written authorization from the Owner, instruct the Contractor to order such special inspection, testing or approval, and the Contractor shall give notice as in Subparagraph 7.8.1. If such special inspection or testing reveals a failure of the Work to comply with the requirements of the Contract Documents or, with respect to the performance of the Work, with laws, ordinances, rules, regulations or orders of any public authority having jurisdiction, the Contractor shall bear all costs thereof, including the Architect's additional services made necessary by such failure; otherwise the Owner shall bear such costs, and an appropriate Change Order shall be issued.

7.10 ARBITRATION

7.10.1 All claims, disputes and other matters in question arising out of, or relating to, this Contract or the breach thereof, except as set forth in Subparagraph 2.2.9 with respect to the Architect's decisions on matters relating to artistic effect, and except for claims which have been waived by the making or acceptance of final payment as provided by Subparagraphs 9.7.5 and 9.7.6, shall be decided by arbitration in accordance with the Construction Industry Arbitration Association then obtaining unless the parties mutually agree otherwise. This agreement so to arbitrate shall be specifically enforceable under the prevailing arbitration law. The award rendered by the arbitrators shall be final, and judgment may be entered upon it in accordance with applicable law in any court having jurisdiction thereof.

9.3 PROGRESS PAYMENTS

9.3.3 The Contractor warrants and guarantees that title to all Work, materials and equipment covered by an Application for Payment, whether incorporated in the Project or not, will pass to the Owner upon the receipt of such payment by the Contractor, free and clear of all liens, claims, security interests or encumbrances, hereinafter referred to in this Article 9 as "liens"; and that no Work, materials or equipment covered by an Application for Payment will have been acquired by the Contractor, or by any other person performing the Work at the site or furnishing materials and equipment for the Project, subject to an agreement under which an interest therein or an encumbrance thereon is retained by the seller or otherwise imposed by the Contractor or such other person.

9.7 SUBSTANTIAL COMPLETION AND FINAL PAYMENT

9.7.1 When the Contractor determines that the Work or a designated portion thereof acceptable to the Owner is substantially complete, the Contractor shall prepare for submission to the Architect a list of items to be completed or corrected. The failure to include any items on such list does not alter the responsibility of the Contractor to complete all Work in accordance with the Contract Documents. When the Architect on the basis of an inspection determines that the Work is substantially complete, he will then prepare a Certificate of Substantial Completion, which shall state the responsibilities of the Owner and the Contractor for maintenance, heat, utilities, and insurance, and shall fix the time within which the Contractor shall complete the items listed therein, said time to be within the Contract Time unless extended pursuant to Paragraph 8.3. The Certificate of Substantial Completion shall be submitted to the Owner and the Contractor for their written acceptance of the responsibilities assigned to them in such Certificate.

10.2 SAFETY OF PERSONS AND PROPERTY

10.2.1 The Contractor shall take all reasonable precautions for the safety of, and shall provide all reasonable protection to prevent damage, injury or loss to:

    .1 all employees on the Work and all other persons who may be affected thereby.

    .2 all the Work and all materials and equipment to be incorporated therein, whether in storage on or off the site, and

    .3 other property at the site or adjacent thereto, including trees, shrubs, lawns, walks, pavements, roadways, structures and utilities not designated for removal, relocation or replacement in the course of construction.

10.2.2 The Contractor shall comply with all applicable laws, ordinances, rules, regulations and orders of any public authority having jurisdiction for the safety of persons or property or to protect them from damage, injury or loss. He shall erect and maintain, as required by existing conditions and progress of the Work, all reasonable safeguards for safety and protection, including posting danger signs and other warnings against hazards, promulgating safety regulations and notifying owners and users of adjacent utilities.

11.3 PROPERTY INSURANCE

11.3.4 The Owner shall file a copy of all policies with the Contractor prior to commencement of the Work. If the Owner does not do so, the Contractor may then effect insurance which will protect the interests of himself, his Subcontractors and the Sub-subcontractors in the Work, and by appropriate Change Order the cost thereof shall be charged to the Owner.

12.1 CHANGE ORDERS

12.1.6 Should concealed conditions encountered in the performance of the Work below the surface of the ground be at variance with the conditions indicated by the Contract Documents or, should unknown physical conditions below the surface of the ground of an unusual nature, differing materially from those ordinarily encountered and generally recognized as inherent in the Work of the character provided for in this Contract, be encountered, the Contract Sum shall be equitably adjusted by Change Order upon claim by either party made within a reasonable time after the first observance of the conditions.

THE STANDARD FORM OF AGREEMENT BETWEEN OWNER AND CONTRACTOR

THE AIA SHORT FORM CONTRACT FOR

SMALL CONSTRUCTION CONTRACTS

WHERE THE BASIS OF PAYMENT IS A

STIPULATED SUM

FOR OTHER CONTRACTS THE AIA ISSUES THE STANDARD FORMS OF OWNER-CONTRACTOR AGREEMENTS AND THE STANDARD GENERAL CONDITIONS FOR THE CONSTRUCTION OF BUILDINGS FOR USE IN CONNECTION THEREWITH

THIS AGREEMENT

made the   day of   in the year Nineteen Hundred and

BY AND BETWEEN

hereinafter called the Owner, and

hereinafter called the Contractor.

WITNESSETH,

That the Owner and the Contractor, for the considerations hereinafter named agree as follows:

ARTICLE 1. SCOPE OF THE WORK—
The Contractor shall furnish all of the material and perform all of the work for

as shown on the Drawings and described in the Specifications entitled

prepared by   Architect
all in accordance with the terms of the Contract Documents.

ARTICLE 2. TIME OF COMPLETION— The work shall be commenced and completed as follows:

ARTICLE 3. CONTRACT SUM—The Owner shall pay the Contractor for the performance of the Contract subject to the additions and deductions provided therein in current funds, the sum of

dollars. ($)

ARTICLE 4. PROGRESS PAYMENTS—The Owner shall make payments on account of the contract, upon requisition by the Contractor, as follows:

ARTICLE 5. ACCEPTANCE AND FINAL PAYMENT—Final payment shall be due   days after completion of the work, provided the contract be then fully performed, subject to the provisions of Article 16 of the General Conditions.

ARTICLE 6. CONTRACT DOCUMENTS—Contract Documents are as noted in Article 1 of the General Conditions. The following is an enumeration of the drawings and specifications:

ARTICLE 1. CONTRACT DOCUMENTS

The contract includes the AGREEMENT and its GENERAL CONDITIONS, the DRAWINGS, and the SPECIFICATIONS. Two or more copies of each, as required, shall be signed by both parties and one signed copy of each retained by each party.

The intent of these documents is to include all labor, materials, appliances and services of every kind necessary for the proper execution of the work, and the terms and conditions of payment therefor.

The documents are to be considered as one, and whatever is called for by any one of the documents shall be as binding as if called for by all.

ARTICLE 2. SAMPLES

The Contractor shall furnish for approval all samples as directed. The work shall be in accordance with approved samples.

ARTICLE 3. MATERIALS, APPLIANCES, EMPLOYEES

Except as otherwise noted, the Contractor shall provide and pay for all materials, labor, tools, water, power and other items necessary to complete the work.

Unless otherwise specified, all materials shall be new, and both workmanship and materials shall be of good quality.

All workmen and sub-contractors shall be skilled in their trades.

ARTICLE 4. ROYALTIES AND PATENTS

The Contractor shall pay all royalties and license fees. He shall defend all suits or claims for infringement of any patent rights and shall save the Owner harmless from loss on account thereof.

ARTICLE 5. SURVEYS, PERMITS, AND REGULATIONS

The Owner shall furnish all surveys unless otherwise specified. Permits and licenses necessary for the prosecution of the work shall be secured and paid for by the Contractor. Easements for permanent structures or permanent changes in existing facilities shall be secured and paid for by the Owner, unless otherwise specified. The Contractor shall comply with all laws and regulations bearing on the conduct of the work and shall notify the Owner if the drawings and specifications are at variance therewith.

ARTICLE 6. PROTECTION OF WORK, PROPERTY, AND PERSONS

The Contractor shall adequately protect the work, adjacent property and the public and shall be responsible for any damage or injury due to his act or neglect.

ARTICLE 7. ACCESS TO WORK

The Contractor shall permit and facilitate observation of the work by the Owner and his agents and public authorities at all times.

ARTICLE 8. CHANGES IN THE WORK

The Owner may order changes in the work, the Contract Sum being adjusted accordingly. All such orders and adjustments shall be in writing. Claims by the Contractor for extra cost must be made in writing before executing the work involved.

ARTICLE 9. CORRECTION OF WORK

The Contractor shall re-execute any work that fails to conform to the requirements of the contract and that appears during the progress of the work, and shall remedy any defects due to faulty materials or workmanship which appear within a period of one year from the date of completion of the contract. The provisions of this article apply to work done by subcontractors as well as to work done by direct employees of the Contractor.

ARTICLE 10. OWNER'S RIGHT TO TERMINATE THE CONTRACT

Should the Contractor neglect to prosecute the work properly, or fail to perform any provision of the contract, the Owner, after seven days' written notice to the Contractor, and his surety if any may, without prejudice to any other remedy he may have, make good the deficiencies and may deduct the cost thereof from the payment then or thereafter due the contractor or, at his option, may terminate the contract and take possession of all materials, tools, and appliances and finish the work by such means as he sees fit, and if the unpaid balance of the contract price exceeds the expense of finishing the work, such excess shall be paid to the Contractor, but if such expense exceeds such unpaid balance, the Contractor shall pay the difference to the Owner.

ARTICLE 11. CONTRACTOR'S RIGHT TO TERMINATE CONTRACT

Should the work be stopped by any public authority for a period of thirty days or more, through no fault of the Contractor, or should the work be stopped through act or neglect of the Owner for a period of seven days, or should the Owner fail to pay the Contractor any payment within seven days after it is due, then the Contractor upon seven days' written notice to the Owner, may stop work or terminate the contract and recover from the Owner payment for all work executed and any loss sustained and reasonable profit and damages.

ARTICLE 12. PAYMENTS

Payments shall be made as provided in the Agreement. The making and acceptance of the final payment shall constitute a waiver of all claims by the Owner, other than those arising from unsettled liens or from faulty work appearing thereafter, as provided for in Article 9, and of all claims by the Contractor except any previously made and still unsettled. Payments otherwise due may be withheld on account of defective work not remedied, liens filed, damage by the Contractor to others not adjusted, or failure to make payments properly to subcontractors or for material or labor.

ARTICLE 13. CONTRACTOR'S LIABILITY INSURANCE

The Contractor shall maintain such insurance as will protect him from claims under workmen's compensation acts and other employee benefits acts, from claims for damages because of bodily injury, including death, and from claims for damages to property which may arise both out of and during operations under this contract, whether such operations be by himself or by any subcontractor or anyone directly or indirectly employed by either of them. This insurance shall be written for not less than any limits of liability specified as part of this contract. Certificates of such insurance shall be filed with the Owner and architect.

ARTICLE 14. OWNER'S LIABILITY INSURANCE

The Owner shall be responsible for and at his option may maintain such insurance as will protect him from his contingent liability to others for damages because of bodily injury, including death, which may arise from operations under this contract, and any other liability for damages which the Contractor is required to insure under any provision of this contract.

ARTICLE 15. FIRE-INSURANCE WITH EXTENDED COVERAGE

The Owner shall effect and maintain fire insurance with extended coverage upon the entire structure on which the work of this contract is to be done to one hundred per cent of the insurable value thereof, including items of labor and materials connected therewith whether in or adjacent to the structure insured, materials in place or to be used as part of the permanent construction including surplus materials, shanties, protective fences, bridges, temporary structures, miscellaneous materials and supplies incident to the work, and such scaffoldings, stagings, towers, forms, and equip-

OWNER-CONTRACTOR AGREEMENT

ment as are not owned or rented by the contractor, the cost of which is included in the cost of the work. EXCLUSIONS: The insurance does not cover any tools owned by mechanics, any tools, equipment, scaffolding, staging, towers, and forms owned or rented by the Contractor, the capital value of which is not included in the cost of the work, or any cook shanties, bunk houses or other structures erected for housing the workmen. The loss, if any, is to be made adjustable with and payable to the Owner as Trustee for the insureds and contractors and subcontractors as their interests may appear, except in such cases as may require payment of all or a proportion of said insurance to be made to a mortgagee as his interests may appear.

Certificates of such insurance shall be filed with the Contractor if he so requires. If the Owner fails to effect or maintain insurance as above and so notifies the Contractor, the Contractor may insure his own interests and that of the subcontractors and charge the cost thereof to the Owner. If the Contractor is damaged by failure of the Owner to maintain such insurance or to so notify the Contractor, he may recover as stipulated in the contract for recovery of damages. If other special insurance not herein provided for is required by the Contractor, the Owner shall effect such insurance at the Contractor's expense by appropriate riders to his fire insurance policy. The Owner, Contractor, and all subcontractors waive all rights, each against the others, for damages caused by fire or other perils covered by insurance provided for under the terms of this article except such rights as they may have to the proceeds of insurance held by the Owner as Trustee.

The Owner shall be responsible for and at his option may insure against loss of use of his existing property, due to fire or otherwise, however caused.

If required in writing by any party in interest, the Owner as Trustee shall, upon the occurrence of loss, give bond for the proper performance of his duties. He shall deposit any money received from insurance in an account separate from all his other funds and he shall distribute it in accordance with such agreement as the parties in interest may reach or under an award of arbitrators appointed, one by the Owner, another by joint action of the other parties in interest, all other procedure being as provided elsewhere in the contract for arbitration. If after loss no special agreement is made, replacement of injured work shall be ordered and executed as provided for changes in the work.

The Trustee shall have power to adjust and settle any loss with the insurers unless one of the Contractors interested shall object in writing within three working days of the occurrence of loss, and thereupon arbitrators shall be chosen as above. The Trustee shall in that case make settlement with the insurers in accordance with the directions of such arbitrators, who shall also, if distribution by arbitration is required, direct such distribution.

ARTICLE 16. LIENS

The final payment shall not be due until the Contractor has delivered to the Owner a complete release of all liens arising out of this contract, or receipts in full covering all labor and materials for which a lien could be filed, or a bond satisfactory to the Owner indemnifying him against any lien.

ARTICLE 17. SEPARATE CONTRACTS

The Owner has the right to let other contracts in connection with the work and the Contractor shall properly cooperate with any such other contractors.

ARTICLE 18. THE ARCHITECT'S STATUS

The Architect shall be the Owner's representative during the construction period. He has authority to stop the work if necessary to insure its proper execution. He shall certify to the Owner when payments under the contract are due and the amounts to be paid. He shall make decisions on all claims of the Owner or Contractor. All his decisions are subject to arbitration.

ARTICLE 19. ARBITRATION

Any disagreement arising out of this contract or from the breach thereof shall be submitted to arbitration, and judgment upon the award rendered may be entered in the court of the forum, state or federal, having jurisdiction. It is mutually agreed that the decision of the arbitrators shall be a condition precedent to any right of legal action that either party may have against the other. The arbitration shall be held under the Standard Form of Arbitration Procedure of The American Institute of Architects or under the Rules of the American Arbitration Association.

ARTICLE 20. CLEANING UP

The Contractor shall keep the premises free from accumulation of waste material and rubbish and at the completion of the work he shall remove from the premises all rubbish, implements and surplus materials and leave the building broom-clean.

IN WITNESS WHEREOF the parties hereto executed this Agreement, the day and year first above written.

Owner _____

Contractor _____

OWNER-CONTRACTOR AGREEMENT

CERTIFICATE OF INSURANCE

AIA Document G705

This certifies to the Addressee shown below that the following described policies, subject to their terms, conditions and exclusions, have been issued to:
NAME & ADDRESS
OF INSURED

COVERING (SHOW PROJECT NAME
AND/OR NUMBER AND LOCATION)

Addressee:

Date _____

KIND OF INSURANCE	POLICY NUMBER	Inception Date	Expiration Date	LIMITS OF LIABILITY	
1. (a) Workmen's Comp.				$	Statutory Workmen's Compensation
(b) Employers' Liability				$	One Accident and Aggregate Disease
2. Comprehensive General Liability				$	Each Person—Premises and Operations
				$	Each Person—Elevators
				$	Each Person—Independent Contractors
(a) Bodily Injury Including Personal Injury				$	Each Person—PRODUCTS INCLUDING COMPLETED OPERATIONS
				$	Each Person—Contractual
				$	Each Occurrence—
				$	Aggregate PRODUCTS INCLUDING COMPLETED OPERATIONS
				$	Each Occurrence—Premises—Operations
				$	Each Occurrence—Elevators
				$	Each Occurrence—INDEPENDENT CONTRACTOR
(b) Property Damage				$	Each Occurrence—PRODUCTS INCLUDING COMPLETED OPERATIONS
				$	Each Occurrence—Contractual
				$	Aggregate—
				$	Aggregate OPERATIONS PROTECTIVE PRODUCTS AND CONTRACTUAL
3. Comprehensive Automobile Liability (a) Bodily Injury				$	Each Person
				$	Each Occurrence—
(b) Property Damage				$	Each Accident—

4.

UNDER GENERAL LIABILITY POLICY OR POLICIES

Yes   No

1. Does Property Damage Liability Insurance shown include coverage for XC and U hazards? . . . _____ _____
2. Is Occurrence Basis Coverage provided under Property Damage Liability? . . . . _____ _____
3. Is Broad Form Property Damage Coverage provided for this Project? . . . . _____ _____
4. Is Personal Injury Coverage included? . . . . _____ _____
5. Is coverage provided for Contractual Liability (Indemnification Clause) assumed by insured? . . _____ _____

UNDER AUTOMOBILE LIABILITY POLICY OR POLICIES

1. Does coverage shown above apply to non-owned and hired automobiles? . . . . _____ _____
2. Is Occurrence Basis Coverage provided under Property Damage Liability? . . . . _____ _____

In the event of cancellation, fifteen (15) days written notice shall be given to the party to whom this Certificate is addressed.

NAME OF INSURANCE COMPANY _____

ADDRESS _____

SIGNATURE OF AUTHORIZED REPRESENTATIVE _____

12

GENERAL REQUIREMENTS

The General Requirements of the specifications consist of certain sections listed under Division 1 of the Uniform System (see Chapter 17). The sections recommended by the Uniform System for inclusion under this division are the following:

1. Summary of the Work
2. Schedules and Reports
3. Samples and Shop Drawings
4. Temporary Facilities
5. Cleaning-up
6. Project Closeout
7. Allowances
8. Alternates

Since the General Requirements and the proposed Sections included therein are of a relatively recent innovation (October 1966), they have not yet been exposed to widespread use and experience. The recommendations originally suggested under the CSI Format, which were promulgated in July 1964 for inclusion under the General Requirements, consisted of Alternates, Alterations, Inspections, Tests, Allowances, and Temporary Facilities. From the standpoint of time and usage the value of some of the sections proposed under the Uniform System is yet to be determined.

The original purpose of the General Requirements in the CSI Format was to provide a place for the non-legal, non-technical requirements which are required by the contractor in order to construct the project. All of those requirements of a general nature not suitable for inclusion under the technical sections were also expected to be set forth here by the early proponents of the CSI Format. As stated in Chapter 11, the Supplementary Conditions had become the catch-all section in which were specified temporary utilities, temporary facilities, and a host of other requirements not of a legal nature. It was the intention that the establishment of a division entitled "General Requirements" would create a convenient place for instructions to the contractor that could not logically be placed anywhere else.

Section 1A—
Summary of the Work

The first section recommended under the Uniform System is entitled "Summary of the Work." It further proposes that it summarize the work under the contract, work under other contracts related to the project, work and equipment to be provided by the owner, work to be postponed to a date later than the designated completion date, and whether the work is to be completed under a single or segregated contract.

129

Generally, the majority of projects undertaken by architects are concerned with a single contract for a single building. In very many instances, where the foregoing is the condition, the proposed section, "Summary of the Work," can be safely omitted, since there is no information to be transmitted to the contractor which is not already understood or stated elsewhere. The bidding requirements, specifically the invitation to bid, and the bid form establish the fact that there is but one contract, and the time of completion in the bid form would indicate whether any work were to be postponed beyond the designated completion date. The work under the contract is clearly defined by the drawings and specifications and so, in effect, a "Summary of the Work" in the majority of cases would simply be a duplication of information.

It is recommended that this section be used only when there are involved, segregated contracts with varying completion dates, and that the information be limited to a tabulation of these items so that there is no possibility of error in the repetition of information.

Section 1B— Schedules and Reports

The second section, "Schedules and Reports," recommended under the Uniform System is a convenient and logical place for the enumeration of items related to the following major headings:

> Reference Standards
> Standard Abbreviations
> Sub-Surface Soil Reports
> Progress Photographs
> Critical Path Schedules and Reports
> Certification of Lines and Levels
> Schedule of Tests
> Testing Agencies
> Color Schedule

Reference Standards

The following language is suggested for this heading:
All references to codes, specifications and standards referred to in the specifications or shown on the drawings shall mean and intend to be the latest edition, amendment and revision of such reference standard in effect as of the date of these specifications and drawings.

Abbreviations

The following language is suggested for this heading:
Reference to a technical society, institution, association or governmental authority is made in the specifications in accordance with the following abbreviations:

130

AAMA	Architectural Aluminum Manufacturers Association
AASHO	American Association of State Highway Officials
ACI	American Concrete Institute
AIA	American Institute of Architects
AIEE	American Institute of Electrical Engineers
AISC	American Institute of Steel Construction
AISI	American Iron and Steel Institute
ALS	American Lumber Standards
APA	American Plywood Association
ATI	Asphalt Tile Institute
ASHRAE	American Society of Heating, Refrigerating and Air Conditioning Engineers
ASME	American Society of Mechanical Engineers
ASTM	American Society for Testing and Materials
AWI	Architectural Woodwork Institute
AWPA	American Wood-Preservers' Association
AWPI	American Wood Preservers Institute
AWS	American Welding Society
CS	Commercial Standard, U.S. Dept of Commerce
FGJA	Flat Glass Jobbers Association
FS	Federal Specification
GA	Gypsum Association
IES	Illuminating Engineering Society
MIA	Marble Institute of America
MLMA	Metal Lath Manufacturers Association
MS	Military Specification
MSTD	Military Standard
NAAMM	The National Association of Architectural Metal Manufacturers
NHLA	National Hardwood Lumber Association
NBFU	National Board of Fire Underwriters
NBS	National Bureau of Standards
NEC	National Electric Code of NBFU
NFPA	National Fire Protection Association
NLMA	National Lumber Manufacturers Association
NTMA	The National Terrazzo and Mosaic Association, Inc.
NWMA	National Woodwork Manufacturers Association
SDI	Steel Deck Institute
SSPC	Steel Structures Painting Council
SCPI	Structural Clay Products Institute

SPR	Simplified Practice Recommendation, U.S. Dept. of Commerce
TCA	Tile Council of America
UL	Underwriters' Laboratories, Inc.
USA	United States of America Standards Association

Sub-Surface Soil Reports Under this heading, the architect may include the boring locations and the log of the borings unless this information is already incorporated on one of the drawings, in which case this paragraph may be omitted, or a simple reference to its location on the drawings noted herein.

Progress Photographs The following paragraph or modification thereof concerning progress photographs may be incorporated under this heading:

a. During the progress of the Work, the Contractor shall have photographs taken once a month, consisting of 3 views, all taken where directed by the Architect. The prints shall be 8 in. x 10 in., linen backed. At the completion of all Work five final photographs shall be taken as directed by the Architect.

b. One print of each photograph shall be mailed to the Owner and 2 prints to the Architect. The photographs shall be neatly labeled, dated and identified in a title box in the lower right-hand corner, showing:

(1) Date of exposure
(2) Project name and location
(3) Direction of view

c. Except as may be otherwise directed, all negatives shall be retained by the photographer until completion of the work, at which time they shall become the property of the Owner, and the Contractor shall obtain and deliver the same to the Owner.

Critical Path Schedules and Reports If a CPM schedule is warranted or required, the detailed provisions concerning its execution should be described here. In the absence of a CPM schedule, the details and provisions for a monthly progress schedule should be outlined under this heading:

A suggested paragraph for a progress schedule is as follows:
Progress Schedule:
In order to facilitate coordination and fitting, the General Contractor shall prepare a "Plan of Operations and Progress Schedule" which shall show concisely the manner in which

Work will be started, prosecuted, the inter-relationship of the work under the various Contracts, times upon which different phases of the Work are to be started, methods and speed for progressing the different phases and dates upon which the certain sub-contracts are dependent upon that under other sub-contracts. The Plan of Operations and Progress Schedule shall be "weighed" to schedule each trade in proportion to the entire project, both physically and financially.

In preparing the above Plan of Operations and Progress Schedule, the Contractor shall assure that the methods, dates and other pertinent matter are acceptable to the Architect and, when completed, he shall submit to and obtain approval from the Architect.

After approval of the above Plan of Operations and Progress Schedule, the Contractor shall be responsible for seeing that it is adhered to and for ascertaining that proper coordination is maintained between work of all Contracts.

Certification of Lines and Levels

Under this heading the following paragraph may be incorporated:
a. The Contractor shall furnish certification from a licensed surveyor who shall verify periodically that all portions of the work are located in accordance with the drawings and at the required elevations. Upon completion of foundation walls, the Contractor shall prepare and deliver to the Architect a certified survey showing that all dimensions, elevations, and angles and the location of the building is in accordance with the contract drawings. When all enclosing walls are completed, a further survey shall be supplied, certifying the location and plumbness of such walls.

b. The surveyor selected for the above purpose shall be subject to the approval of the Architect. All surveys shall be furnished to the Architect for delivery to the Owner.

Schedule of Tests

Under this heading it is recommended that a tabulation be made of the tests required under the various technical sections. This information in effect is a checklist for the architect and the contractor, summarizing the tests specified under several Sections. One can arrange this information as follows:

Section	Par. & Description
2A Earthwork	2A. 5. Compaction Tests
3A Concrete	3A. 6. Concrete Tests
4A Masonry	4A. 7. Tests of Mortar
4A Masonry	4A. 8. Tests of Brick

Testing Agencies   Under this paragraph the architect may list those preselected independent testing agencies which are acceptable to him for testing of the various materials or components or he may establish the criteria for their selection by the contractor. To avoid any conflict of interests or possible collusion, it is recommended that the architect or engineer preselect the independent testing agency and for the owner to pay for the cost. The cost may be paid directly by the owner, or an allowance may be set up in the specifications against which the testing agency costs are drawn and paid for.

A representative illustration for specifying the requirements of a Testing Agency is as follows:

Testing Agency
a. The (Contractor shall) (Owner will) retain the services of an independent testing laboratory to perform the tests and make the required inspections and reports as specified in the various sections of the specifications or as required by the architect in case of question as to the strength or suitability of materials. Testing laboratories shall be responsible for conducting and interpreting the tests; shall state in each report whether or not the specimens tested conform to all requirements of the Contract Documents; shall specifically note deviations, if any, from said requirements. The testing of piping and pressure vessels as specified under the mechanical sections of the specifications shall be done by the Contractor and witnessed by the Architect. The (Contractor shall) (Owner will), except as otherwise specified, pay for all required laboratory services and tests. All testing laboratories shall be subject to the Architect's approval.

b. The nature and scope of testing services performed by an agency retained by the Contractor shall be in accordance with requirements of governing authorities having jurisdiction over the work and as otherwise specified, and shall be consistent with reasonable standards of engineering practice.

Color Schedule   In many instances an architect issues a color schedule at the time of bidding. This practice eliminates many problems that arise during the course of construction when such a schedule is not available. Colors for some materials influence their cost, and unless these are known in advance of bidding, extras may be encountered later if special colors or premium colors are required. While the Uniform System shows the color schedule as a paragraph under the section, ' Schedules and Reports," it might be more convenient to establish the color schedule as a separate section under Division 1. Since it can be quite long and is usually referred to quite often, a separate section would make it more convenient for use on the project.

The third Section recommended under the Uniform System is entitled "Samples and Shop Drawings." Such a system has several advantages over the methods generally employed.

When samples and shop drawings are listed in one section, there is more control in the office and in the field, since this section forms a check list for all concerned and there is only one source for reference. When samples and shop drawings are listed under the several sections, variations may occur in the number of samples or copies required, the place where they are to be approved, and the manner of submission.

Another recommendation offered refers to the manner in which shop drawings are submitted for approval. In lieu of submitting four, five, or six copies for approval, a reproducible ozalid is submitted. The reproducible copy is marked and corrected by the architect. He strikes off as many copies as he needs for himself, sends the reproducible ozalid back to the contractor, who strikes off his copy, and then on to the subcontractor, who makes copies for his own needs. This system reduces the clerical work involved in transposing corrections to the various copies, with possibility of committing errors, and also reduces the time required to log in and log out the several copies of each drawing.

The following section represents a guide specification for sample and shop drawings. All that is needed is simply a reference under each technical section to this section, if samples and shop drawings are required.

Section 1C—Samples and Shop Drawings
1C. 1. General
a. Article 4.13 of the AIA General Conditions are modified as follows:

b. The Contractor shall provide samples and shop drawings listed below and those requested under the mechanical specifications sections, in accordance with the following specifications. No materials shall be used which do not equal the approved samples. Until such approval has been given, any materials or appliances to be so approved must not be fabricated or incorporated in the work. The approval or acceptance of samples will not preclude the rejection of any material upon the discovery of defects in same prior to the final acceptance of the completed work. After a material has been approved, no change in brand or make will be permitted unless satisfactory written evidence is presented to, and approved by, the Architect that the manufacturer cannot make scheduled delivery of approved material, or that material delivered has been rejected and the substitution of a suitable material is an urgent necessity, or that other conditions are apparent which indicate the approval of such substitute materials to be in the best interest of the Owner. Samples, shop drawings, material lists, manufacturers' literature, and other required information shall be submitted in sufficient time to permit proper consideration and action on same before any materials and items—which such samples, shop drawings, and information represent—are delivered on the work. All samples of materials requiring laboratory tests shall be submitted to the laboratory for testing, not less than 90 days before such materials are required to be used in the work. All other samples, manufacturers' literature, and other sample information shall be submitted for approval not less than 30 days before such materials are required to be used in the work. The Contractor will be held responsible for any delay in the progress of the work which may be due to his failure to observe these requirements, and the time for the completion of his Contract will not be extended on account of his failure to submit samples and shop drawings promptly in strict accordance therewith.

1C. 2. Samples

a. Samples shall be submitted in duplicate and manufacturers' literature and material lists in quadruplicate, except where a greater or lesser number is specifically required by the specifications.

b. Samples must be submitted by the Contractor only, unless he has authorized his subcontractor to submit them and has notified the Architect to this effect. Such samples shall be shipped (prepaid) by the Contractor.

c. Samples will receive consideration only when covered by a letter signed by the Contractor. This letter shall contain a list of samples, the name of the project, Contractor, manufacturer, brand, and quarry; also the job number, the specifications paragraph numbers to which samples refer, the ASTM or Federal Specifications Number (if any), and such additional information as many be required by the specifications for the particular material being furnished. Copy of the letter must be enclosed with the samples, and any samples received without the identification letter will be considered "unclaimed goods" and held for a limited time only. Any deviation from contract requirements shall be so stated in the letter of transmittal.

d. Each sample and manufacturers' literature shall be labeled to indicate the name of the project, name of Contractor, manufacturer, brand, quarry, job number, and Federal Specification or ASTM Number where required. In addition, catalogs shall be marked to indicate the specific items submitted for approval.

e. Samples which are rejected by the Architect must be resubmitted as soon as possible after notification of the rejection, and shall be marked "Resubmitted Sample" in addition to the other information required on the label.

f. In connection with the mechanical work of the project (plumbing, heating, electrical work, etc.), the Contractor shall submit a complete list of materials and other required information, as listed under the respective mechanical sections of the specifications, within 30 days after date of notice to proceed; no consideration will be given to partial lists submitted from time to time.

g. Where an asterisk (*) occurs before a material, the Contractor may submit brand name, manufacturers' literature, and manufacturers' certificate of compliance with contract requirements in lieu of samples.

h. The right is reserved to require submission of samples of any material or any material lists, whether or not particularly mentioned herein.

1C.3. Shop Drawings
a. The Contractor shall submit one copy of shop, erection, or setting drawings required. Such shop, erection, and setting drawings shall be ozalids that are acceptable, legible, and reproducible ozalid (sepia) prints with positive side up for the purpose of annotation and correction by the Architect. Drawings shall be submitted rolled within a mailing tube, fully protected for shipment. After approval by the Architect, each party receiving the drawing will strike off the required num-

ber of copies for his own records. A space of 4 in. x 4 in. shall be reserved on each ozalid print to accommodate the Architect's approval or rejection stamp. These drawings and details shall be submitted sufficiently in advance of the work which they cover, and in accordance with a prearranged schedule, to afford ample time for checking, correcting, and rechecking— if necessary for such drawings and details; no claim for delay will be granted the Contractor if caused by his failure to comply with the requirements of this Section.

b. Before submitting shop drawings for approval, the Contractor shall check the shop drawings of subcontractors for accuracy, shall ascertain that all work contiguous with and having bearing on other work shown on shop drawings is accurately drawn, and that the work shown is in conformity with the contract requirements.

c. All such drawings and details at the time of submission must bear the stamp of approval of the Contractor as evidence that such drawings and details have been checked by the Contractor. Any drawings submitted without such executed stamp of approval, or whenever it is evident (despite the stamp) that the drawings have not been checked, they will be returned to the Contractor for resubmission and will not be considered; in such event, it will be deemed that the Contractor has not complied with this article and the Contractor shall bear the risk of all delays to the same extent as if no drawings or details at all had been submitted.

d. The Contractor shall prepare composite drawings and installation layouts, when required, to solve tight field conditions. Such drawings are to consist of dimensioned plans and elevations, and must give complete information, particularly as to size and location of sleeves, inserts, attachments, openings, conduits, ducts, boxes, structural interference, etc.

e. These composite shop drawings and field installation layouts shall be co-ordinated in the field by the Contractor and his subcontractors for proper relationship to the work of other trades, based on field conditions, and shall be checked and approved by them before submission to the Architect for his final approval. The Contractor shall have competent technical personnel readily available for such co-ordinating and checking, as well as for the supervision of the field installation of the work in accordance with the shop drawings and field installation layouts, which have been previously determined by him to be correct and carry the Architect's approval stamp.

f. In instances where the work of more than one Contractor is involved, except as in (2) below, the General Contractor shall prepare and submit composite drawings that show and define the work under all affected contracts or trades, shall submit such drawings to the Architect and obtain approval thereof and, after approval, shall distribute prints of approved drawings to all affected Contractors.

   (1) Affected Contractors and trades shall co-operate in the preparation of above composite drawings to assure proper co-ordination between all trades.

   (2) Whenever only the mechanical and/or the electrical work is involved, the composite drawings referred to above shall be prepared by the heating and ventilating contractor, and it shall be his responsibility to see that the work is co-ordinated with that of all other trades affected.

g. The submission of shop drawings (in either the original submission or when resubmitted with corrections) constitutes evidence that the Contractor has checked all information thereon, and that he accepts and is willing to perform the work, as shown, in a workmanlike manner and in accordance with the best standard practice. No claim for an extra shall be based on work shown on shop drawings, unless such claim is noted on the Contractor's transmittal letter accompanying the shop drawings.

h. The cost of any changes in construction due to improper checking and co-ordination by the Contractor shall be paid for by that Contractor, and said Contractor shall be responsible for all additional costs, including co-ordination.

i. Upon receipt of shop drawings, the Architect will assign a file number thereto. The Contractor, in any subsequent correspondence, shall refer to this file and identification number assigned by the Architect to expedite replies relative to previously approved or rejected shop drawings.

1C.4. Shipping Address
The following items shall be sent to the Architect;

_____
(name)

_____
(address)

The samples and shop drawings are then listed in the numerical order of the Specification Sections. A typical listing follows:

MASONRY SECTION NO. _____.

1. SAMPLES

Cast stone, each kind, 8 in. x 8 in. x 4 in.
Cut stone, each kind, 8 in. x 8 in. x 4 in.
Face brick, showing quality
*Glass Block
Granite, 8 in. x 8 in. x 4 in., each kind, showing finishes
Structural facing tile

2. MANUFACTURERS' LITERATURE

Calking compound
Fire brick
Mortar ingredients

3. SHOP DRAWINGS

Complete cutting and setting drawings of all stonework, showing jointing, bonding, anchorage, and connection with other work, including full size details of moldings and ornament.

Section 1D— Temporary Facilities The fourth Section recommended under the Uniform System is entitled "Temporary Facilities." A suggested Section is as follows:

Section 1D—Temporary Facilities

1D.1. General

The term "Contractor" as used throughout this Section shall mean the General Contractor unless otherwise noted. The Contractor shall pay all costs for such temporary facilities until such time as provided for in the AIA General Conditions, Article 9.7.1.

1D.2. Signs

a. No signs or advertisements will be allowed to be displayed on the premises without the approval of the Architect.

b. Construction sign(s) shall be subject to the approval of

the Architect and the Owner. Text and lettering shall be as provided for at a later date.

c. Lettering for all building signs and elsewhere as noted or required shall conform to a uniform standard throughout the building, as directed by the Architect, and in accordance with approved samples and / or shop drawings.

1D.3. Temporary Elevator

a. Temporary elevator shall be provided for necessary service during construction operations, after the hoistway enclosures are completed and electrical power is available, using temporary machines at the Contractor's option, or using permanent machines if they are available in due time for the required services.

b. The temporary elevator shall include temporary wood cars and suitable gates including temporary hoistway doors, all designed in accordance with the local and State safety requirements.

c. The temporary service shall include qualified operating and maintenance personnel to perform the work in connection with the temporary operations.

d. Upon completion of temporary use, all worn or damaged parts are to be replaced and all equipment placed in first-class condition equal to new.

e. The cost of all the foregoing and every other cost incident to such temporary operation shall be borne by the Contractor.

1D.4. Temporary Field Offices

a. The Contractor shall provide and maintain a field office with telephone at the job site. In addition, the Contractor shall provide a temporary office with not less than 200 sq. ft. of space for the use of the Architect at the construction site. The Architect's office shall be complete with light, heat, air conditioning, telephone, electric water cooler, plan racks, 4-drawer metal file, tables, chairs, etc. and janitor service. When it becomes possible to establish an office in the building, office accommodation of approximately the same size as those in the field offices, including the above services shall be provided and maintained for the Architect until the issuance of a Certificate of Substantial Completion. Field and temporary offices shall be removed when no longer required. The Contractor shall pay for all costs in connection with the construction, servicing, maintenance and removal of temporary offices.

b. Construction shanties, sheds and temporary facilities provided as required above or for the Contractor's convenience shall be located and constructed as approved by the Architect and maintained in good condition and neat appearance, including painting with two coats of approved paint of a color as selected by the Architect.

1D.5. Temporary Heat

a. The Contractor shall furnish temporary heat during the progress of construction of the building until the building is enclosed.

1. The building shall be considered enclosed when it has reached the stage when all exterior walls have been erected, when the roof has been substantially completed, all exterior openings closed up either by the permanently glazed windows and doors, or by adequate and approved temporary closing and the building is ready for interior masonry and plastering operations.

2. The temporary heating to be furnished by the Contractor before the building is enclosed shall be by devices approved by the Architect. The use of salamanders is prohibited unless specifically approved by the Architect and its operation constantly supervised by the Contractor. The Contractor shall pay for all fuel, maintenance and attendance required thereby.

b. After the building has been enclosed, the Contractor shall furnish temporary heating for all trades of all Contracts to maintain temperatures of at least 50°F., except:

1. During the placing, setting and curing of plaster, ceramic tile, quarry tile, terrazzo, etc., maintain minimum of 65°, maximum of 75°F. After plastering has commenced, and until the project is complete, reasonably uniform temperatures and acceptable humidity shall be maintained in the 65°-75° range to prevent cracks caused by overheating or by colder temperatures.

2. For a period of at least ten days prior to the placing of interior wood and throughout the placing of this material, painting, varnishing and floor laying, and until completion and acceptance by the Owner and Architect; provide a temperature in the spaces involved of not less than 70°F.

3. See individual technical sections for other temperature requirements.

c. Specifically the Contractor shall provide a complete system of temporary heat to protect the enclosed building from freezing and to expedite the construction of the work. The Contractor may utilize the new heating equipment to accomplish the specified heating results.

d. The Contractor shall provide temporary heating during normal working hours, which will be from 7:45 a.m. to 4:45 p.m. The Contractor shall also provide sufficient temporary heat during non-working hours as directed.

e. The cost of temporary heating shall be included in the Contractor's bid.

f. Upon the conclusion of the temporary heating period, the Contractor shall remove all temporary piping, temporary radiators, etc. The Contractor shall bear all expenses required for repairing any damage incurred by him during the temporary heating period caused by the installation or removal of temporary heating equipment.

1D.6. Temporary Light And Power

a. For construction of the building, the Contractor shall make all arrangements with the Electric Utility Company to provide adequate electric service for all temporary light and power as hereinafter indicated.

b. The Contractor shall provide, install and maintain the temporary lighting and power systems from points of the Utility Company to provide the following:

1. Safety and watchmen's lighting on all stairs, other locations requiring same, and ample lighting in the rooms of the building.

2. Convenience outlets so that the center of any room or

143

space will be not more than distance of the length of a standard trailer as set forth in the local Electrical Workers and Contractor's Agreements. Those convenience outlets shall be provided as the work progresses and as required by the various Contractors on the Project.

c. The light outlets shall consist of left-hand threaded sockets, 100 watt lamps, and lamp guards. Provide wiring, service and control switches and fuse protection to comply with all local, State and Underwriters' codes, rules and regulations.

d. Hours of regular service shall be from 7:45 a.m. to 4:45 p.m. on regular working days.

e. For work on the building, at times other than as set forth above, any sub-contractor requiring lighting or power shall arrange for such service, and pay for same, including current consumption.

f. Trailers for use in convenience outlets shall be provided by the trades using or requiring same.

g. The permanent installation may be used for temporary work.

h. The cost of temporary light and power including current shall be included in the Contractor's bid.

i. Power tools not exceeding 1 h.p. each may be operated from the temporary electric system.

1. Each subcontractor shall, at his own expense, furnish, install and maintain all power wiring and all equipment necessary to supply power for tools exceeding 1 h.p. each for his work and, upon completion of his work, shall remove any temporary power lines installed by him. Each subcontractor shall pay for the electric energy consumed by him for such power, and shall, at his own expense, furnish the metering equipment, make the applications, and obtain the permits necessary to supply such power.

1D.7. Temporary Roads And Access To Site

a. The Contractor shall construct and maintain in good usable condition, all required temporary roads and access to site and, when no longer required, shall remove all temporary construction, and restore the site.

b. Access to the site for delivery of construction material and / or equipment shall be made only from locations approved by the Architect.

1D.8. Temporary Stairs, Ladders, Ramps, Hoists, Runways, Etc.

a. The Contractor shall furnish and maintain all equipment such as temporary stairs, ladders, ramps, scaffolds, hoists, runways, derricks, chutes, etc., as required for the proper execution of the work.

b. All such apparatus, equipment and construction shall meet all requirements of the Labor Law and other State or local laws applicable thereto.

c. As soon as permanent stairs are erected, the Contractor shall provide temporary protective treads, handrails, and shaft protection.

1D.9. Temporary Toilets

The Contractor shall provide and maintain in a sanitary condition enclosed weather-tight toilets for the use of all construction personnel at a location within the contract limits, complete with fixtures, water and sewer connections and all appurtenances as approved by the Architect. Upon completion of the work, toilets and their appurtenances shall be removed. These installations shall be in accordance with all applicable codes and regulations of authorities having jurisdiction. Chemical toilets will be permitted. The number of toilet rooms required shall be in accordance with USA Standard Safety Code for Building Construction or other local authorities.

1D.10. Temporary Water Supply

The Contractor shall provide and maintain, or arrange to have provided and maintained a temporary water service to the facilities of the water company and in such form approved by that company. He shall extend therefrom a supply adequate for all construction purposes and inclusive of two branches, each centralizing in different parts of the project so as to be convenient for all trades. He shall pay for all water used; protect the lines against freezing and be fully responsible for the temporary installation in every way. He shall provide any and all hose needed.

1D.11. Watchman

The Contractor shall supply sufficient and approved watchmen service to prevent illegal entry or damage during nights, holidays and other periods when work is not being prosecuted.

1D.12. Protective Covering

a. The Contractor shall protect all finished surfaces, including the jambs and soffits of all openings used as passageways or through which materials are handled, against any possible damage resulting from the conduct of work by all trades.

b. All finished surfaces, including factory-finished and job-finished items, shall be clean and not marred upon delivery of the building to the Owner. The Contractor shall, without extra compensation, refinish all such spaces where such surfaces prove to have been inadequately protected and are damaged.

c. Tight wood sheathing shall be laid under any materials that are stored on finished cement surfaces. Reinforced non-staining kraft building paper and plywood or planking must be laid over all types of finished floor surfaces in traffic areas and before moving any material over these finished areas. Wheelbarrows, if used over such areas, shall have rubber tired wheels.

d. Roof surfaces shall not be subjected to traffic nor shall they be used for storage of material. Where some activity must take place in order to carry out the Contract, adequate protection, subject to approval by the Architect, shall be provided.

Section 1E— Cleaning Up The fifth section recommended under the Uniform System is entitled "Cleaning Up." This is an extension of the more general provisions included under the AIA General Conditions, Article 4.16. It is not intended to cover that type of cleaning which is usually concerned with specific trade functions, such as clearing and grubbing as specified under Earthwork; removal of excess excavation specified under Earthwork; cleandown of brickwork specified under Masonry; and cleandown of ceramic tile specified under Tile Work. Rather it is a housekeeping function related to daily removal of trash and debris and the cleaning of surfaces upon final acceptance.

With the AIA General Conditions it is possible to include the following provisions for cleaning up under the Supplementary Conditions rather than as a separate Section under Division 1:

Article 4.16 "Cleaning Up" of the AIA General Conditions shall be supplemented as follows:

4.16.3. No rubbish shall be allowed to accumulate or be allowed to remain on the premises or job site beyond a reasonable length of time. Particular attention shall be given to this requirement.

4.16.4. All rubbish shall be lowered by way of chutes or taken down on hoists or lowered in receptacles. Under no circumstances shall any rubbish or waste be dropped or thrown from one level to another within or outside the building.

4.16.5. Immediately after unpacking materials, all packing case lumber or other packing materials, excelsior, wrappings and other like flammable wastes shall be collected and removed from the building and premises.

4.16.6. Care shall be taken by all workmen not to mark, soil or otherwise deface any finish or plastering. In the event that any finish or plastering becomes defaced in any way by mechanics or workmen, the Contractor or any of his sub-contractors shall clean and restore such surfaces to their original condition.

4.16.7. Each subcontractor engaged upon the work shall bear his full responsibility in cleaning up immediately upon completion of his work in accordance with all provisions under this heading and he shall cooperate with the Contractor to that effect; this shall in no way be construed to relieve the Contractor of his responsibility for leaving all work in a clean and proper condition, satisfactory to the Owner and the Architect.

4.16.8. Before final acceptance of the work, all ceiling and wall surfaces, floors, window and door frames, hardware, metal work, glass, equipment, etc. shall be thoroughly cleaned as required. Glass shall be cleaned on both sides. Glass damaged in cleaning shall be replaced by the Contractor at his expense.

Section IF— Project Closeout

The sixth Section recommended under the Uniform System is entitled "Project Closeout." This section, in effect, should be a tabulation of those items specified throughout the documents which have a bearing on the contractor's final submissions. It also permits the architect to certify as to the contractor's Substantial Completion and to issue the final Certificate for Payment, as provided for in the AIA General Conditions.

Those items which should be delivered to the architect for transmission to the owner at the close of the project, and which should be spelled out under this section, include the following:

Release or Waiver of Liens	— AIA General Conditions Article 9.7.3.
Guarantees	— All guarantees in excess of one year stipulated under the various technical sections.
As-Built or Record Drawings	— Generally required under the mechanical sections.
Maintenance Manuals	— For operating equipment usually specified under the mechanical and electrical sections.
Certificate of Occupancy	— Where local laws require this certificate, specify that it be obtained by the contractor.

Section 1G—Allowances   The seventh section recommended under the Uniform System is entitled "Allowances." The AIA General Conditions, Article 4.8, "Cash Allowances," sets forth the criteria governing its application. The Uniform System suggests that a tabulation of the dollar amounts set forth under each of the separate technical sections be made under this section.

It is questionable whether a separate section should be written covering this tabulation. A choice may be made to include a paragraph under the Supplementary Conditions which, in effect, supplements the provisions of the General Conditions.

The current edition of the AIA General Conditions clarifies an area concerning cash allowances that was rather vague under previous editions. This has to do with whether the cash allowance is simply for purchase of an item, or whether it includes delivery and installation. The new language is quite explicit; it states that "these allowances shall cover the net cost of the materials and equipment delivered and unloaded at the site, and all applicable taxes. The Contractor's handling costs on the site, labor, installation costs, overhead, profit and other expenses shall be included in the Contract Sum and not in the allowance."

In spite of this language which identifies what the allowance includes, there may still be inequities. A cash allowance for brick without stating its size or even its moisture absorption characteristics does not give the contractor sufficient information on installation costs. Size of brick is a factor in laying up masonry, and likewise, its moisture absorption rate has an effect on how many can be laid. Hardware is another example. A mortise lock costs more to install than a cylindrical lock set. It is therefore good practice to give additional information concerning an item purchased by the allowance method, to permit the contractor to evaluate the cost of installation more equitably.

The eighth section recommended under the Uniform System is **Section 1H—** entitled "Alternates." A separate section for alternates provides **Alternates** for an all inclusive listing of the alternates and an opportunity to describe them in detail. The individual technical sections do not always permit an appropriate place for the description of an alternate material, since they may be entirely unrelated to that technical section. For example, if terrazzo is scheduled as an alternate for vinyl asbestos tile, it cannot be specified under vinyl asbestos. By utilizing one section for all alternates, the numbers can be established, together with their headings, and these numbers and headings can be tabulated in the bid form quite briefly, as illustrated in Chapter 10.

Detailed requirements for alternates related to mechanical and electrical work can be specified under their respective technical sections, with brief references made thereto under the section, "Alternates."

A suggested format for a section on alternates follows:

Section 1H—Alternates

1H.1. General
All work of this Section shall be performed in accordance with the requirements of the Contract Documents.

1H.2. Scope
Furnish all labor, materials, plant, tools, services and equipment necessary for proper and complete execution of accepted alternates. Amount of alternate prices to be added to or deducted from the Base Bid shall be stated on the Bid Form and shall include cost of any and all modifications made necessary by Owner's acceptance of Alternate.

Alternate No. 1—Vinyl Asbestos Tile

a.   State the amount to be deducted from the Base Bid if vinyl asbestos tile is used in all corridors in lieu of terrazzo as indicated in Finish Schedule.

b.   Vinyl asbestos tile shall conform to FS SS-T-312, 9 in. x 9 in. x ⅛ in., manufacturer's standard color as selected.

c.   Install in accordance with the requirements of the Vinyl Asbestos Tile Association.

Alternate No. 2—Stainless Steel Elevator Entrances

a.   State the amount to be added to the Base Bid if stainless steel is used for elevator entrances, in lieu of baked enamel hollow metal.

b.   Stainless steel shall be type 302, 14 U.S. gage, with a No. 4 finish.

Alternate No. 3—Emergency Generator

a.   State the amount to be added to the Base Bid if Emergency Generator as specified in Section 16L is furnished and installed.

Section 1J— Alterations   The Uniform System does not list alterations anywhere. There is, however, a need to describe this work, which occurs quite frequently. Since the nature of alterations involves many trades, and since it is preferable to write a performance rather than a descriptive type of specification for this work, a general section under Division 1 places the responsibility directly on the contractor to coordinate the various activities of the subcontractors involved in this operation.

Most drawings for alterations simply indicate existing partitions to be removed or an existing door or window to be removed and blocked in, without any additional details. The specifications, too, for this work usually refer to matching existing conditions, so that the work of alterations cannot usually be described specifically, but must be covered generally.

A specification for alterations which has been used quite successfully, states in general performance-type language the requirements, as follows:

Section 1J—Alterations

1J.1. General

All work of this Section shall be performed in accordance with the requirements of the Contract Documents.

IJ.2. Scope

The work covered by this Section of the Specifications shall include the furnishing of all plant, labor, equipment, appliances, and materials and the performing of all operations in connection with alterations, removal and demolition work, complete, in strict accordance with this Section of the Specifications and the applicable drawings.

1J.3. General Requirements

a. Alterations shall be as indicated on the drawings and in accordance with applicable technical sections of the Specifications. The Contractor shall do all necessary demolition or removal of existing work as required in connection with this project, including shoring, bracing, etc., and removal of unwanted material and debris from the site. This work shall be done in a most careful manner, as the Contractor will be held responsible for any damage which may be caused thereby to any part or parts of existing structure. Debris shall be kept damp to keep down dust. Chutes shall be used for removal of demolished materials from upper levels.

b. Portions of the existing structure where existing work is to be demolished or removed, and where new work is to be done, connections made, materials handled, or equipment moved and relocated, shall be temporarily protected. Temporary protection shall be such that the interior of existing structure will at all times be protected from dust and weather inclemency, and interior heat conserved. Suitable temporary dustproof barrier partitions with hinged doors shall be provided in the existing structure where and as directed and approved by the Architect. Temporary openings in exterior walls shall be protected by temporary weatherproof plywood closures. The Contractor will be held responsible for any damage to the existing structure or contents by reason of the insufficiency of such protection.

c. The Contractor shall furnish and install adequate guards, barricades and other temporary protection to prevent injury to persons.

d. Where alterations occur, or new and old work join, the im-

151

mediate adjacent surfaces, or so much thereof as is required by the involved conditions, shall be cut, removed, patched, repaired or refinished, and left in as good a condition as existed prior to the commencing of the work. The materials and workmanship employed in the alterations involving new construction, unless otherwise shown or specified, shall conform to that of the original work. Each Contractor shall perform that portion of the alteration work which is generally performed by his trades and subcontractors.

e. Where required by the drawings or specifications, certain materials and equipment shall be relocated as shown or specified. Refinishing of certain existing surfaces shall be as hereinafter specified. All relocated materials and equipment shall be repaired and refinished as necessary to leave the finished work in good condition.

f. Salvaged materials accruing from the work wrecked or removed under this Contract shall become the property of the Contractor (unless otherwise noted in the Specifications or drawings to remain the property of the Owner) and shall be removed by him from the Site. Salvaged material specified or noted on the drawings to be retained by Owner, shall be protected and stored where directed. General construction equipment and mechanical and electrical equipment remaining the property of the Owner shall be carefully removed by the Contractor and shall be stored by him on the Site where directed, except that such items indicated or specified to remain or be relocated shall be set and connected in the indicated location.

1J.4. Scheduling Of Alteration And Demolition Work

a. Before commencing any alteration, removal and demolition work, the Contractor shall prepare and submit for approval by the Architect and Owner a schedule showing the commencement, the order and the completion dates of the various parts of this work.

b. Before starting any work relating to existing utilities (electrical, sewer, water, heat, gas, fire lines, etc.) that will temporarily discontinue or disrupt service to the existing buildings, the Contractor will be required to give 72 hours notice to the Architect and the Owner and obtain their approval in writing before proceeding with this phase of the work.

13

SPECIFICATION WRITING

PROCEDURES

How does one write a specification? The uninitiated practitioner faced with the task of writing a specification for his first project does what all other beginners have done who have not had a basic understanding of the principles of specification writing. In his emergency, he begs from some friend of older practice the specifications of another undertaking as like in character to his own as he can find, and then cuts, pastes, writes in, and crosses out as well as he knows how, to make a patchwork that will apply more or less well, to the structure he has planned.

However, armed with the principles of specification writing, the task becomes less onerous and more manageable. A system of specification writing procedures should include the work preliminary to the actual writing of the specifications, the outline or preliminary specification, the sources of information, the form and arrangement of the specifications, the actual writing of the specifications, and finally, the reproduction and binding of the specifications. These procedures deal with time-tested methods such as the use of guide or master specifications, check lists, work sheets, and catalog files.

Reduced to their simplest form, specifications should be written according to an organized system. A good draftsman will develop systematic methods of laying out his drawings. A good office will have logical standards for indication of doors, windows, and the other countless elements of the drawings. Similarly, a specification writer must have a system for the preparation of specifications, especially since they must be written after the drawings have progressed to a point where they are about fifty percent completed and the time available to write and complete the specifications is scant. The pressure of time thus makes a systematic approach essential.

One of the first documents that the specification writer should have is preliminary, or outline, specifications. This is generally prepared by the project architect or designer with the collaboration of the specification writer, and briefly lists materials and finishes without describing workmanship or fabrication. The next step is to prepare a complete take-off of every item from the working drawings, and—in conjunction with a standard checklist and the Uniform System described in Chapter 17—establish the technical sections.

With the technical sections established on the basis of the preliminary takeoff, the specifier is now in a position to start and complete some sections, and to start and gather information on other sections, or do research on some materials where he does not have sufficient information. The nature of specification writing is such that one cannot start writing immediately and continue until the project is completed. There will be need for conferences with the job captain and designer to arrive at decisions on many items, and it will be necessary to obtain information from manufacturers and their representatives on materials and products when the architectural details involving these items are in doubt and require clarification and research.

There are many sections that can be written on the basis of incomplete drawings. These should be written at the outset, since they are not likely to change during the development of the drawings. Such sections include those under Division 9, "Finishes," for example—ceramic tile, terrazzo, resilient flooring, acoustic treatment. Other sections which may be written around partially completed drawings will include earthwork, concrete, toilet partitions, and masonry.

To write these sections, many specification writers will have their own "guide" or "master" specifications, which they have carefully developed over the years. To be truly effective, these guides should not be static, and should be revised as dictated by experience and new developments. Some people refer to these guides as "canned specifications." However, it is difficult to see how any specification writer can do without such a valuable tool, which comprises the sum total of his experiences and his best efforts to write better specifications.

Specification writers, like any other individuals, naturally develop their own personal idiosyncrasies with respect to the systems they will develop in organizing themselves, their work habits, and their approach to the task of writing specifications. Some use card systems on which they develop standard paragraphs, others use collections of notes, and checklists. Whatever system is employed, it should be orderly and systematic.

The following principles will aid the beginner in establishing a procedure for writing his specifications when he approaches the task before him.

1. Review the preliminary or outline specifications to obtain a better understanding of the project.

2. Review the preliminary drawings to visualize the project and obtain a better insight.

3. Since the architectural specification writer is the focal point for all of the specifications, determine who the consultants are for the structural, mechanical, electrical, and site specifications. Coordinate their activities and establish the form, arrangement, and numbering systems of the technical sections. To insure coordination between the respective sections so that there is no duplication or overlapping, submit a coordination list (see exhibit at end of this chapter) to all the consultants for agreement on what goes where.

4. Review the working drawings and prepare a table of contents of the technical sections. (See Chapter 17 for typical section titles.)

5. Make a take-off from the drawings of all the items, and list them on work sheets under the appropriate section titles. For example, under the section title "Miscellaneous Iron and Steel," make a listing of such items as railings, ladders, stairs, saddles, gratings, and mesh partitions, and indicate the drawings on which the details occur so that they can be easily found again when the final specification is written.

6. Discuss questions relating to any of these items with the job captain, designer, or any other individual, and determine what will be shown on the drawings and what will be specified (see Chapter 2). Determine which items require additional research, note these, and perform the necessary investigation at a time when a lack of sufficient drawings preclude actual writing of specifications.

7. Commence the actual writing of the specifications. Use guide or master specifications where these are available, and utilize the take-off list and a checklist to insure completeness of each section.

8. Select those sections which will not be affected by further development of the drawings as previously described, and complete these sections. Start those sections on which there is a good deal of information that can be gleaned from the drawings, and note the information that will be required in order to complete them at a later date. Arrange the information within each section as described in Chapter 5.

9. Do the required research on unknowns when you can no longer proceed with any actual specification writing.

10. Leave until the very last those sections which require almost complete working drawings, such as carpentry and millwork, and miscellaneous and ornamental metal.

SAMPLE CHECKLIST

PROJ. NO._____

Project_____

Project Architect_____

Mechanical & Electrical Consultants_____

Structural Consultants_____

Site Consultants_____

ITEMS TO BE COORDINATED BETWEEN
GENERAL CONSTRUCTION, MECHANICAL
AND ELECTRICAL SPECIFICATIONS

F-GC = Furnished by General Contractor's Trades

I-GC = Installed by General Contractor's Trades

F-M&E = Furnished by Mechanical or Electrical Contractors'
        Trades

I-M&E = Installed by Mechanical or Electrical Contractors'
        Trades

(Indicate by GC, M or E in space to indicate who does what)

ITEM	F-GC	I-GC	F-M&E	I-M&E	REMARKS
1. Temporary Heat	___	___	___	___	_____
2. Temporary Water	___	___	___	___	_____
3. Temporary Light and Power	___	___	___	___	_____
4. Emergency Lighting	___	___	___	___	_____
5. Temporary Toilets	___	___	___	___	_____

F-GC I-GC F-M&E I-M&E REMARKS

F-GC I-GC F-M&E I-M&E REMARKS

ITEM	F-GC	I-GC	F-M&E	I-M&E	REMARKS
6. Excavation and Backfill Inside Buildings for M & E Work	___	___	___	___	_____
7. Excavation and Backfill Outside Building for M & E Work	___	___	___	___	_____
8. Keeping Site and Excavations Free from Water	___	___	___	___	_____
9. Subsoil Drainage Inside Building	___	___	___	___	_____
10. Subsoil Drainage Outside Building	___	___	___	___	_____
11. Footing Drains	___	___	___	___	_____

12. Manholes
    (a) Electrical
    (b) Storm
    (c) Sewer
    (d) Steam
13. Drywells
14. Roof Vent Pipe Flashing
    a. Cap Flashing
    b. Base Flashing
15. Roof Curb Flashing
    a. Cap Flashing
    b. Base Flashing
16. Roof Drain Flashing
17. Shower Stall Pan
    Flashing
18. Concrete Foundation
    Pads, Pits, etc., In-
    side Buildings for
    M & E Work
19. Concrete Foundation
    Pads, Cradle for Fuel
    Oil Tank, etc. Outside
    Building
20. Prime Painting of
    M & E Work
21. Finish Painting of
    M & E Work
22. Color Coding and
    Banding of M & E Work
23. Ornamental HVAC Grilles
24. Exterior Wall Louvers
    (a) Connected to Ducts
25. Wall and Ceiling Access
    Panels and Supporting
    Frames therefor
26. Plaster Rings for
    Lighting Fixtures
27. Incinerator
28. Elevators
29. Mechanical Stairs
30. Dumbwaiters
31. Sidewalk Lifts
32. Moving Walks
33. Linen and Garbage
    Chutes
34. Window Washing Machines
35. Toilet Room Accessories
36. Prefabricated Showers

37. Chimney Breeching Frame _____ _____ _____ _____ _____
38. Chimney Cleanout Door _____ _____ _____ _____ _____
39. Prefabricated Chimney _____ _____ _____ _____ _____
40. Convector Enclosures _____ _____ _____ _____ _____
    (a) Ornamental _____ _____ _____ _____ _____
41. Pit Covers _____ _____ _____ _____ _____
42. Catwalks to Mechanical
    Equipment _____ _____ _____ _____ _____
43. Ladders to Mechanical
    Equipment and Valves _____ _____ _____ _____ _____
44. Lightning Protection _____ _____ _____ _____ _____
45. Fire Extinguishers _____ _____ _____ _____ _____
    (a) In Boiler Room _____ _____ _____ _____ _____
46. Fire Extinguisher
    Cabinets _____ _____ _____ _____ _____
47. Kitchen Range Hoods _____ _____ _____ _____ _____
48. Dishwashing Hoods _____ _____ _____ _____ _____
49. Walk-in Refrigerator _____ _____ _____ _____ _____
50. Prefab. Walk-in
    Refrigerator _____ _____ _____ _____ _____
51. Exterior Transformer
    Vault _____ _____ _____ _____ _____
52. Watchmen's System _____ _____ _____ _____ _____
53. X-Ray Equipment _____ _____ _____ _____ _____
54. Sterilizing Equipment _____ _____ _____ _____ _____
55. Laboratory and Pharmacy
    Equipment _____ _____ _____ _____ _____
56. Communications _____ _____ _____ _____ _____
57. Food Service Equipment _____ _____ _____ _____ _____
58. Laundry Equipment _____ _____ _____ _____ _____
59. Clocks _____ _____ _____ _____ _____
60. Pneumatic Tube System _____ _____ _____ _____ _____
61. Hydrotherapy Equipment _____ _____ _____ _____ _____
62. Surgical Lights _____ _____ _____ _____ _____
63. Thermal Insulation for
    Boiler Room Ceiling _____ _____ _____ _____ _____

14

SPECIFICATION REFERENCE

SOURCES

The scope of architectural specifications is so broad—encompassing the gamut of materials from acoustical products through zinc coatings—that no single specification writer can possibly have a complete and intimate knowledge of all these materials, nor of the constant improvements which manufacturers are continually making. Knowing where to look for information is half the battle; applying that information successfully is the other half. The specification writer should familiarize himself with these specification reference sources and learn to differentiate between the good and the not too useful material available, since the latter will simply clutter his files. These technical references should be accumulated and made a part of a ready reference file for the specification writer's use.

Specification reference sources fall into several categories, as follows:

      1. Text books
      2. Materials Standards
      3. Guide Specifications
      4. Journals and Periodicals
      5. Building Codes and Ordinances
      6. Materials Investigations
      7. Association Standards
      8. Manufacturers' Catalog Files
      9. General References

Text Books

Text books serve as a valuable source of information on specification principles. Since specification writing is an art, not a science, the authors have expressed many opinions which are frequently at variance with one another. The student and the professional specification writer can assess for himself the arguments for and against various systems outlined therein, and determine for himself the methods which he will employ in writing his own specifications.

The following text books are suggested as a reference source:

H. G. Edwards	**Specifications** D. Van Nostrand Co.
D. W. Gale	**Specifying Building Construction** Reinhold Publishing Corporation
G. Goldsmith	**Architects' Specifications and How to Write Them** American Institute of Architects

H. R. Sleeper **Architectural Specifications**
John Wiley & Sons

D. A. Watson **Specifications Writing for Architects and Engineers**
McGraw-Hill Book Co.

Materials Standards Standards for materials have been devised and issued by governmental agencies, by national technical associations, and by certain producers of materials, in order to provide uniform standards as to criteria, grading, and testing. The specification writer should obtain indices listing the various standards promulgated by these agencies and associations, in order to secure those which will be useful to him in his work. The specification reference sources for these materials standards are as follows:

American Society for Testing & Materials
1916 Race Street, Philadelphia, Pa.

Federal Specifications
U.S. Superintendent of Documents
Washington, D.C. 20402

Simplified Practice Recommendations
Dept. of Commerce
U.S. Superintendent of Documents
Washington, D.C. 20402

Commercial Standards
Dept. of Commerce
U.S. Superintendent of Documents
Washington, D.C. 20402

United States Standards
United States of America Standards Association
10 East 40th Street, New York, N.Y. 10016

Guide Specifications Guide, or master, specifications for technical sections, and technical reports that may serve as an aid in the preparation and development of specifications, can be obtained from the following sources:

Specification Work Sheets
American Institute of Architects
1735 New York Avenue
Washington, D.C. 20006

CSI Manual of Practice and Specification Series
Construction Specifications Institute
1717 Massachusetts Avenue N.W.
Washington, D.C. 20036

Valuable information and discussions on current technical problems written by individuals proficient in various areas of construction materials and techniques are frequently published in the following journals and periodicals:

Building Research
Building Research Institute
1725 De Sales Street N.W.
Washington, D.C. 20036

Construction Specifier
Construction Specifications Institute
1717 Massachusetts Avenue N.W.
Washington, D.C. 20036

Canadian Building Digest
National Research Council
Ottawa, Canada

There are codes and ordinances promulgated by official bodies, cities, and municipalities which have been developed to safeguard health, life, and property. These include zoning regulations, building codes, fire, safety, plumbing, and electrical codes. These codes should be consulted to insure compliance with them, and by incorporating them into the specifications by reference where necessary. Occasionally these codes may cover only minimum standards and types of construction, and the architect or specification writer may prefer to specify a higher grade of construction than that required under the codes. Reference sources often used when no code prevails, or when a better type of construction is desired, are the following codes:

National Building Code
National Board of Fire Underwriters
85 John Street, New York, N.Y. 10038

Uniform Building Code
International Conference of Building Officials
50 South Los Robles
Pasadena, Calif.

Basic Building Code
Building Officials Conference of America
1313 East 60th Street
Chicago, Illinois

Southern Standard Building Code
Southern Building Code Congress
1116 Brown-Marx Building
Birmingham, Alabama

National Electric Code
National Board of Fire Underwriters
85 John Street, New York, N.Y. 10038

National Plumbing Code
United States of America Standards Association
10 East 40 Street, New York, N.Y. 10016

Materials Investigations   Another valuable service that has been performed by some governmental agencies and by national technical associations is the laboratory investigation of properties of building materials and the structural elements of buildings, as well as the performance of mechanical equipment for buildings. Many of these reports have also been compiled on the basis of the experience record of many individuals who have had close association with certain materials. These specification reference sources are:

Building Materials and Structures Reports
National Bureau of Standards
U.S. Superintendent of Documents
Washington, D.C. 20402

Building Science Series
National Bureau of Standards
U.S. Superintendent of Documents
Washington, D.C. 20402

Housing Research Papers
Housing & Home Finance Agency
Washington, D.C. 20402

The Wood Handbook
Forest Products Laboratory
U.S. Department of Agriculture
Madison, Wisconsin

Reports
Small Homes Council
University of Illinois
Urbana, Illinois

Other very pertinent sources of architectural information may be found in standards issued by various manufacturing, contracting, and technical associations, as follows:

ACI Standards
American Concrete Institute
Box 4754 Redford Station
Detroit, Michigan 48219

Metal Curtain Wall Manual
National Association of Architectural Metal Manufacturers
228 North LaSalle Street
Chicago, Illinois 60601

Glazing Manual
Flat Glass Jobbers Association
6210 West 10 Street
Topeka, Kansas 66615

**Recommended Specifications for Lathing, Furring
  and Plastering**
Contracting Plasterers & Lathers International Association
1343 H Street, N.W.
Washington, D.C. 20005

Technical Notes—Brick & Tile
Structural Clay Products Institute
1520-18th Street N.W.
Washington, D.C. 20036

Manufacturers' Catalog Files

Manufacturers' catalogs represent another specification reference source. The suggested specifications in manufacturer's catalogs should be used with caution by specification writers. While some publications include manufacturer's specifications which are actually drawn, others are vague, and so written as to exclude certain items of work, and leave much to be desired in the way of precise, informative, and clear subject matter and specifications.

It is absolutely essential, in using specifications contained in manufacturers' catalogs, to be very discriminating in copying them verbatim. Do not use any clauses as written unless every statement is clearly understood. Modify the language where necessary to insure competition and complete understanding.

Many of these catalogs are contained in the following major publications of manufacturers' literature:

Sweets Architectural File
F. W. Dodge Corp.
330 West 42 Street, New York, N.Y. 10018

A-E-C Western Catalog File
Times-Mirror Press
1115 South Boyle Street, Los Angeles, California

General References Additional reference sources for materials, workmanship, standards, tests, and general information are contained in the publications of various associations of manufacturers, technical societies, and contractors' associations. As an aid in quickly locating these sources of information, they have been arranged in accordance with the Uniform System as follows:

Division 1—General Requirements
American Arbitration Association
140 West 51 Street
New York, N. Y. 10020

American Society of Safety Engineers, Inc.
5 North Wabash Avenue
Chicago, Ill. 60602

Builders Exchange
2565 St. Mary's Avenue
Omaha, Nebr. 68100

Factory Insurance Assn.
85 Woodland Street
Hartford, Conn. 06102

Factory Mutual System
Factory Mutual Engineering Division
1151 Boston-Providence Turnpike
Norwood, Mass. 02062

Division 2—Site Work
American Assn. of Nurserymen
Suite 835, Southern Building
Washington, D.C. 20005

American Concrete Pipe Assn.
1815 North Fort Myer Drive
Arlington, Va. 22209

Asphalt Institute
Asphalt Institute Building
College Park, Md. 20740

Division 3—Concrete
American Concrete Institute
Box 4754, Redford Station
Detroit, Mich. 48219

Concrete Industry Board, Inc.
51 East 42 Street
New York, N.Y. 10017

Concrete Reinforcing Steel Institute
228 North La Salle Street
Chicago, Ill. 60601

Expanded Shale, Clay & Slate Institute
1041 National Press Building
Washington, D.C. 20004

Gypsum Roof Deck Foundation
1201 Waukegan Road
Glenview, Ill. 60025

Lightweight Producers Assn.
546 Hamilton Street
Allentown, Pa. 18101

Mo-Sai Institute, Inc.
P.O. Box 5229
Seattle, Wash. 98107

National Ready Mixed Concrete Assn.
900 Spring Street
Silver Spring, Md. 20910

National Sand & Gravel Assn.
900 Spring Street
Silver Spring, Md. 20910

Portland Cement Assn.
33 West Grand Avenue
Chicago, Ill. 60610

Prestressed Concrete Institute
205 West Wacker Drive
Chicago, Ill. 60610

Vermiculite Institute
208 South LaSalle Street
Chicago, Ill. 60604

Division 4—Masonry
Barre Granite Assn., Inc.
51 Church Street
Barre, Vt.

Building Stone Institute
420 Lexington Avenue
New York, N.Y. 10017

Clay Flue Lining Institute
Elephant Road, M.R-1
Perkasie, Pa.

Facing Tile Institute
333 North Michigan Avenue
Chicago, Ill. 60601

Indiana Limestone Institute of America, Inc.
431 South College Avenue
Bloomington, Ind. 47401

Marble Institute of America, Inc.
Room 848, Pennsylvania Building
425 13th Street N.W.
Washington, D.C. 20004

National Cinder Concrete Products Assn.
Box 67
Primrose, Pa. 19019

National Concrete Masonry Assn.
2009 14th Street North
Arlington, Va. 22201

Structural Clay Products Institute
1520 18th Street N.W.
Washington, D.C. 20036

Division 5—Metals; Structural & Miscellaneous
American Hot Dip Galvanizers Assn.
5225 Mauning Place N.W.
Washington, D.C. 20016

American Institute of Steel Construction, Inc.
101 Park Avenue
New York, N.Y. 10017

American Iron & Steel Institute
150 East 42 Street
New York, N.Y. 10017

American Welding Society
345 East 47 Street
New York, N.Y. 10017

American Zinc Institute, Inc.
292 Madison Avenue
New York, N.Y. 10017

Architectural Aluminum Manufacturers Assn.
35 East Wacker Drive
Chicago, Ill. 60601

Metal Roof Deck Technical Institute
53 West Jackson Boulevard
Chicago, Ill.

Porcelain Enamel Institute, Inc.
1900 L Street N.W.
Washington, D.C. 20036

Research Council on Riveted & Bolted Structural Joints
Drexel Institute of Technology, Dept. of Civil Engineering
Philadelphia, Pa. 19104

Steel Joist Institute
Dupont Circle Building
1346 Connecticut Avenue N.W.
Washington, D.C. 20036

Division 6—Carpentry
American Forest Products Industries, Inc.
1816 N Street N.W.
Washington, D.C. 20036

American Hardboard Assn.
Suite 1452, 20 North Wacker Drive
Chicago, Ill. 60606

American Institute of Timber Construction
1757 K Street N.W.
Washington, D.C. 20006

American Plywood Assn.
1119 A Street
Tacoma, Wash. 98401

American Walnut Manufacturers Assn.
666 North Lake Shore Drive
Chicago, Ill.

American Wood-Preservers Assn.
839 17th Street N.W.
Washington, D.C. 20006

Appalachian Hardwood Manufacturers, Inc.
414 Walnut Street
Cincinnati, Ohio 45202

Architectural Woodwork Institute
1808 West End Building
Nashville, Tenn. 37203

Arkansas Soft Pine Bureau
Tower Building
Little Rock, Ark. 72201

California Redwood Assn.
617 Montgomery Street
San Francisco, Calif. 94111

Fine Hardwoods Assn.
666 Lake Shore Drive
Chicago, Ill. 60611

Forest Products Research Society
417 North Walnut Street
Madison, Wis. 53705

Hardwood Dimension Manufacturers Assn.
3813 Hillsboro Road
Nashville, Tenn. 37215

Hardwood Plywood Manufacturers Assn.
2310 South Walter Reed Drive, Box 6246
Arlington, Va. 22206

National Forest Products Assn.
1619 Massachusetts Avenue N.W.
Washington, D.C. 20036

National Hardwood Lumber Assn.
59 East Van Buren Street
Chicago, Ill. 60605

National Particleboard Assn.
711 14th Street N.W.
Washington, D.C. 20005

National Woodwork Manufacturers Assn., Inc.
400 West Madison Street
Chicago, Ill. 60606

Northern Hardwood & Pine Manufacturers Assn.
Suite 207, Northern Building
Green Bay, Wis. 54301

Philippine Mahogany Assn., Inc.
P.O. Box 279
South Pasadena, Calif.

Ponderosa Pine Woodwork Assn.
39 South La Salle Street
Chicago, Ill. 60603

Red Cedar Shingle & Handsplit Shake Bureau
5510 White Building
Seattle, Wash. 98101

Southern Hardwood Lumber Manufacturers Assn.
805 Sterick Building
Memphis, Tenn. 38103

Southern Pine Assn.
520 National Bank of Commerce Building, Box 52468
New Orleans, La. 70150

Vacuum Wood Preservers Institute
5151 Holmes Road
Houston, Texas 77033

West Coast Lumber Inspection Bureau
1410 S.W. Morrison Street
Portland, Ore. 97205

Western Red Cedar Lumber Assn.
4403 White-Henry-Stuart Building
Seattle, Wash. 98101

Western Red & Northern White Cedar Assn.
Box 2576,
New Brighton, Minn. 55112

Division 7—Moisture Protection
Adhesive & Sealant Council
159 North Dearborn Street
Chicago, Ill. 60601

Asphalt Institute
College Park, Maryland 20740

Asphalt Roofing Industry Bureau
Room 2111, 757 Third Avenue
New York, N.Y. 10017

Copper Development Assn.
405 Lexington Avenue
New York, N.Y. 10017

Insulation Board Institute
111 West Washington Street
Chicago, Ill. 60602

Division 8—Doors, Windows, and Glass

American Hardware Manufacturers Assn.
342 Madison Avenue
New York, N.Y. 10017

American Society of Architectural Hardware Consultants
2675 Cleveland Avenue
Santa Rosa, Calif.

Builders Hardware Manufacturers' Assn.
60 East 42 Street
New York, N.Y. 10017

Door Operator & Remote Controls Manufacturers Assn.
110 North Wacker Drive
Chicago, Ill. 60606

Flat Glass Jobbers Assn.
6210 West 10 Street
Topeka, Kansas 66615

Hollow Metal Door Buck Assn.
770 Lexington Avenue
New York, N.Y. 10021

Insect Wire Screening Bureau
441 Lexington Avenue
New York, N.Y. 10017

National Association of Architectural Metal Manufacturers
228 North LaSalle Street
Chicago, Ill. 60601

National Builders Hardware Assn.
1290 Avenue of the Americas
New York, N.Y. 10019

Sealed Insulating Glass Manufacturers Assn.
2217 Tribune Tower
Chicago, Ill. 60611

Stained and Leaded Glass Assn.
40 West 13 Street
New York, N.Y. 10011

Steel Door Institute
2130 Keith Building
Cleveland, Ohio 44115

Steel Window Institute
18455 Harvest Lane
Brookfield, Wis. 53005

Division 9—Finishes
Acoustical Material Assn.
335 East 45th Street
New York, N.Y. 10017

Asphalt & Vinyl Asbestos Tile Institute
101 Park Avenue
New York, N.Y. 10017

Canvas Awning Institute
Box 12287
Memphis, Tenn. 38112

Contracting Plasterers & Lathers Intl. Assn.
1343 H Street N.W., Room 304
Washington, D.C. 20005

Gypsum Assn.
201 North Wells Street
Chicago, Ill. 60606

Gypsum Drywall Contractors International
Suite 201, 127 South Wacker Drive
Chicago, Ill. 60606

Maple Flooring Manufacturers Assn.
424 Washington Avenue
Oshkosh, Wis. 54901

Metal Lath Assn.
636 Engineers Building
Cleveland, Ohio 44114

National Lime Assn.
4000 Brandywine Street N.W.
Washington, D.C. 20016

National Oak Flooring Assn.
814 Sterick Building
Memphis, Tenn.

National Paint, Varnish & Lacquer Assn., Inc.
1500 Rhode Island Avenue N.W.
Washington, D.C. 20005

National Terrazzo & Mosaic Assn., Inc.
1901 Fort Meyer Drive
Rosslyn, Arlington, Va. 22209

Paint & Wallpaper Assn. of America, Inc.
7935 Clayton Road
St. Louis, Mo. 63117

Painting & Decorating Contractors of America
2625 West Peterson Avenue
Chicago, Ill. 60645

Perlite Institution, Inc.
45 West 45 Street
New York, N.Y. 10036

Tile Council of America, Inc.
800 Second Avenue
New York, N.Y. 10017

Vermiculite Assn., Inc.
527 Madison Avenue
New York, N.Y. 10022

Wall Paper Institute
969 Third Avenue
New York, N.Y. 10022

Wood Flooring Institute of America
201 North Wells Street
Chicago, Ill. 60606

Division 10—Specialties

Fire Equipment Manufacturers Assn.
1718 Sherman Avenue
Evanston, Ill. 60201

Gas Appliance Manufacturers Assn., Inc.
60 East 42 Street
New York, N.Y. 10017

National Assn. of Mirror Manufacturers
1225 19th Street N.W.
Washington, D.C. 20036

National Kitchen Cabinet Assn.
918 Commonwealth Building
Louisville, Ky. 40202

Division 11—Equipment

American Home Laundry Manufacturers Assn.
20 North Wacker Drive
Chicago, Ill. 60606

Division 12—Furnishings

American Carpet Institute, Inc.
350 Fifth Avenue
New York, N.Y. 10001

Division 13—Special Construction

Incinerator Institute of America
630 Third Avenue
New York, N.Y. 10017

National Swimming Pool Institute
2000 K Street N.W.
Washington, D.C. 20006

Division 14—Conveying Systems

American Material Handling Society
Suite 306, 1750 Pennsylvania Avenue N.W.
Washington, D.C. 20006

National Assn. of Elevator Contractors
4647 Hampton Avenue
St. Louis, Mo. 63109

National Elevator Manufacturing Industry
101 Park Avenue
New York, N.Y. 10017

Materials Handling Institute, Inc.
Gateway Towers, Gateway Center
Pittsburgh, Pa. 15222

Division 15—Mechanical

American Pipe Fittings Assn.
60 East 42 Street
New York, N.Y. 10017

American Water Works Assn., Inc.
2 Park Avenue
New York, N.Y. 10016

Cast Iron Pipe Research Assn.
Suite 3440, Prudential Plaza
Chicago, Ill. 60601

Cast Iron Soil Pipe Institute
1824-26 Jefferson Place N.W.
Washington, D.C. 20036

Clay Pipe Institute
2600 Wilshire Boulevard
Los Angeles, Calif. 90057

Clay Sewer Pipe Assn., Inc.
300 Cedar Boulevard
Pittsburgh, Pa. 15228

Cooling Tower Institute
4242 Richmond Avenue
Houston, Texas 77027

Home Ventilating Institute
1108 Standard Building
Cleveland, Ohio 44113

Industrial Heating Equipment Assn.
2000 K Street N.W.
Washington, D.C. 20006

National Clay Pipe Institute
1028 Connecticut Avenue N.W.
Washington, D.C. 20036

Division 16—Electrical
American Home Lighting Institute, Inc.
360 North Michigan Avenue
Chicago, Ill. 60601

Illuminating Engineering Research Institute
345 East 47 Street
New York, N.Y. 10017

Illuminating Engineering Society
345 East 47 Street
New York, N.Y. 10017

15

PHYSICAL FORMAT AND STYLE

PHYSICAL FORMAT AND STYLE

15.1 FORMAT AND ARRANGEMENT

a. The format and arrangement of specifications is essential to a workable system. An architect carefully plans his layout of drawings. Plans, elevations, sections, details, and schedules are usually laid out on the drawings in an orderly fashion and the drawing numbers too, follow in certain sequences.

b. An architect should likewise give some thought to the appearances of his specifications and provide for some system in their physical make-up.

15.2 SPECIFICATION SECTIONS

a. The section number and the section title may be arranged, as illustrated for this chapter heading, in capitals and underscored or may appear on one line, as follows:

CHAPTER 15--PHYSICAL FORMAT AND STYLE

15.3 PARAGRAPH HEADINGS

a. In Chapter 5, the observation is made that a technical section in a book of specifications could be considered as analogous to a chapter in a book, and that the breakdown within the section, as in a book, consists of paragraphs and subparagraphs.

b. Each major paragraph heading should be capitalized and underscored and be preceded by the section number, followed by its paragraph number as illustrated for this paragraph 15.3 PARAGRAPH HEADINGS.

15.4 SUBPARAGRAPHS

a. Subparagraph Headings under the major paragraph, such as this one, are written in lower case, continuously underscored with only the first letter of each word capitalized.

b. Other Paragraph Headings: When the heading does not lend itself to a part of the sentence, end the heading with a colon, and write the paragraph in accordance with this illustration.

1. The first subparagraph should be indented and numbered in accordance with this illustration.

(a) A sub-subparagraph would conform to this illustration.

(1) A further subdivision of the paragraph would follow this illustration.

181

c. It is recommended that specifications be written so that there is no necessity to go beyond the order of the subparagraph shown in Par. 15.4b.1.(a)(1). Each paragraph, subparagraph, and sub-subparagraph should be numbered as illustrated to facilitate reference to the specific paragraph in question during correspondence, in addenda, or in discussion. By utilizing the term "paragraph" only, one is not burdened with other systems of nomenclature which refer to articles, headings, paragraphs, categories, and items.

15.5 BLOCK STYLE

a. This style of typing and paragraphing is recommended for specifications, since it is easy to read and permits quick recognition of informaton when it is sought. This chapter is written in the block style. See samples at the end of this chapter.

15.6 PAGE NUMBERING

a. Page Numbers should be used for ready reference. Continuous numbering from cover to cover is a most difficult and time consuming task, and since last minute changes can upset the entire effort, it is recommended that the pages of each section be numbered independently of the others. It is suggested that the page numbers consist of the section number followed by numbers in sequence. The first page of Section 1A would therefor be 1A-1, and succeeding pages of that Section would be 1A-2, 1A-3, etc.

b. Location of Page Numbers: It is recommended that the page number be located at the bottom center of the page. Others may prefer to use the lower right hand or upper right hand corner, which is often used in books.

15.7 CLOSING NOTE

a. Endings of each Section should conclude with a symbol or mark that signifies the end of the Section, such as

***

or

END

SECTION 8A

HOLLOW METAL DOORS AND FRAMES

8A.1 **GENERAL**

 a. All work of this Section shall be performed in accordance with the requirements of the Contract Documents.

Sample Showing Block Form

8A.2 **SCOPE**

 a. Provide all labor, materials, equipment and services and perform all operations required for complete installation of all hollow metal doors and frames and related work as shown on the drawings or specified herein.

8A.3 **WORK OF OTHER SECTIONS**

 a. Furnishing of finishing hardware.

 b. Finish painting.

 c. Rolling metal doors.

8A.4 **MATERIALS**

 a. **Steel**--Prime quality, cold-rolled, pickled, annealed and stretcher-leveled, entirely free from scale, pitting, wave or other defects. Gages refer to the U.S. Standard Gage for Sheet Iron and Steel.

 b. **Structural Steel Shapes** for supporting, reinforcing and attachment work--ASTM A36.

 c. **Fastening Devices**

　1. **Expansion Bolts** shall be galvanized and of approved manufacture.

　2. **Machine Screws**--Fed. Spec. FF-S-92.

　3. **Nuts and Bolts**--ASTM A307.

 d. **Neoprene Gaskets** for sound-insulating doors shall be of approved manufacture, conforming to the requirements of ASTM D735. Grade and Shore Durometer value shall be as recommended by the manufacturer and as approved by the Architect for each use.

 e. **Sound-Deadening and Heat-Retarding Filler** for all hollow metal doors--mineral wool or other insulating material conforming to the requirements of the National Fire Protection Association.

 f. **Paint**

　1. Paint for the rust-inhibitive treatment of reinforcing and attachment steel shall conform to Fed. Spec. TT-P-86c, Type II.

HOLLOW METAL DOORS AND FRAMES

8A.1 <u>GENERAL</u>

(a) All work of this Section shall be performed in accordance with the requirements of the Contract Documents.

8A.2 <u>SCOPE</u>

(a) Provide all labor, materials, equipment and services and perform all operations for complete installation of all hollow metal doors and frames and related work as shown on drawings or specified herein.

8A.3 <u>WORK OF OTHER SECTIONS</u>

(a) Furnishing of finishing hardware.

(b) Finish painting.

(c) Rolling metal doors.

8A.4 <u>MATERIALS</u>

(a) <u>Steel</u>--Prime quality, cold-rolled, pickled, annealed and stretcher-leveled, entirely free from scale, pitting, wave or other defects. Gages refer to the U.S. Standard Gage for Sheet Iron and Steel.

(b) <u>Structural Steel Shapes</u> for supporting, reinforcing and attachment work--ASTM A36.

(c) <u>Fastening Devices</u>

(1) <u>Expansion Bolts</u> shall be galvanized and of approved manufacture.

(2) <u>Machine Screws</u>--Fed. Spec. FF-S-92.

(3) <u>Nuts and Bolts</u>--ASTM A307.

(d) <u>Neoprene Gaskets</u> for sound-isolating doors shall be of approved manufacture, conforming to the requirements of ASTM D735. Grade and Shore Durometer value shall be as recommended by the manufacturer and as approved by the Architect for each use.

(e) <u>Sound-Deadening and Heat-Retarding Filler</u> for all hollow metal doors--mineral wool or other insulating material conforming to the requirements of the National Fire Protection Association.

(f) <u>Paint</u>

(1) Paint for the rust-inhibitive treatment of reinforcing and attachment steel shall conform to Fed. Spec. TT-P-86c, Type II.

SECTION 8A--HOLLOW METAL DOORS AND FRAMES

1. GENERAL

Sample Showing Flush Left Form

All work of this Section shall be performed in accordance with the requirements of the Contract Documents.

2. SCOPE

Provide all labor, materials, equipment and services and perform all operations required for complete installation of all hollow metal doors and frames and related work as shown on the drawings or specified herein.

3. WORK OF OTHER SECTIONS

a. Furnishings of finishing hardware.

b. Finish painting.

c. Rolling metal doors.

4. MATERIALS

a. Steel: Prime quality, cold-rolled, pickled, annealed and stretcher-leveled, entirely free from scale, pitting, wave or other defects. Gages refer to the U.S. Standard Gage for Sheet Iron and Steel.

b. Structural Steel Shapes for supporting, reinforcing and attachment work--ASTM A36.

c. Fastening Devices

(1) Expansion Bolts shall be galvanized and of approved manufacture.

(2) Machine Screws--Fed. Spec. FF-S-92.

(3) Nuts and Bolts--ASTM A307.

d. Neoprene Gaskets for sound-isolating doors shall be of approved manufacture, conforming to the requirements of ASTM D735. Grade and Shore Durometer value shall be as recommended by the manufacturer and as approved by the Architect for each use.

e. Sound-Deadening and Heat-Retarding Filler for all hollow metal doors--mineral wool or other insulating material conforming to the requirements of the National Fire Protection Association.

f. Paint

(1) Paint for the rust-inhibitive treatment of reinforcing and attachment steel shall conform to Fed. Spec. TT-P-86c, Type II.

185

16

BONDS, GUARANTEES, WARRANTIES

Article 7.5 of the AIA General Conditions describes a provision **Surety Bonds** for the furnishing of bonds by a Contractor covering the faithful performance of the Contract and for the payment of obligations arising thereunder. Standard forms have been prepared by the AIA in cooperation with the surety industries and are recommended for use in all private and public construction where a statutory form is not prescribed. These forms are AIA Document A-311, "Performance Bond," and "Labor and Material Payment Bond." Sample copies are illustrated at the conclusion of this chapter.

These Surety Bonds, sometimes called Guarantee Bonds or Construction Bonds, are an essential part of today's construction procedures. They make it possible for the Contractor to provide the Owner with the guarantee of a responsible surety company that he will satisfactorily perform the project at his price and pay his bills. Of additional interest to the Architect is the fact that extra architectural compensation resulting from a Contractor's default caused by delinquency or insolvency is reimbursable by the use of these bonds.

The following extracts from the AIA *Architect's Handbook of Professional Practice,* Chapter 7, September 1963 Edition, provide further insight into Surety Bonds:

Surety Bonds—A Surety Bond is an agreement under which one party, called a 'Surety,' agrees to answer to another party, called an 'Obligee,' for the debt, default, or failure to perform of still another party, called the 'Principal.' As Surety Bonds are used by Architects, the 'Surety' is usually a corporation whose specialty is construction bonds; the 'Obligee' is usually an Owner or a supplier or subcontractor of labor and material to the Contractor; and the 'Principal' ordinarily is the Contractor.

A Bond does not impose on the Surety any obligations which are separate and distinct from or additional to those assumed by the Principal. Under any Surety Bond, the Principal is primarily responsible, and every obligation of the Surety is also that of the Principal. A bond is not a substitute for the integrity, financial worth, experience, equipment, and personnel of the Contractor. Nor is such a bond an independent undertaking by the Surety so long as the Principal performs in accordance with the terms of the Contract.

Contractor Defaults—One of the chief causes for a Contractor's default is the inadequacy of his bid, either on the Owner's Contract or on other past, current, or future Contracts. This may arise from a variety of circumstances such as deficient cost and other accounting records, unforseen price rises, delays, labor troubles, defaults by subcontractors, through disability of the Contractor or key men, lack of adequate working capital, and tax obligations.

Bonds Provide Protection—Bonds, in accordance with the terms of the Contract, provide protection against loss resulting from the failure of others to perform. While the liability of the Principal for damage may be theoretically unlimited, that of the Surety is limited to a certain sum of money called the 'Penalty' or the 'Penal Sum,' which is set out in the bond. The nature of such an instrument is an extension of credit to the Principal, not in the sense of a loan of funds, but rather an endorsement. The Performance Bond directly increases the financial responsibility of the Contractor for the benefit of the Owner by the amount of its Penal Sum.

Relationship to Contracts—Before a client enters into a Building Contract without a Bond it is advisable that the Architect suggest to the Owner that he seek the advice of his legal counsel. If the Owner decides not to require a bond, the Architect should consider writing a letter noting such decision.

No bond can supply the deficiences of an inadequately drawn basic Contract which may not clearly express the intentions of the parties. Even with a good basic Contract, it is well for the Architect to remind the Owner to observe its terms since the Contractor's Surety has relied thereon in its consideration of the risk. If changes of a material nature are to be made during the course of the performance of the Contract, the Surety's consent to such changes is necessary to assure its continued liability under the bond.

Amount of Bonds—A Performance Bond and a Payment Bond, each in the amount of 100% of the Contract Price is recommended. Where a public body is the Owner, the Architect should through legal counsel obtain complete information regarding the legal requirements, amount, form, etc., of the bond.

Statutory and Non-Statutory Bonds—Surety Bonds fall into two categories, statutory and non-statutory or private. Statutory bonds are those given pursuant to law. Since some States have statutory provisions relating to bonds, and since on private projects counsel for the Owner may and very often does express his own ideas regarding the contents of the bond, there is no standard form of Surety Bond applicable to every project. The AIA Document A-311, Performance Bond, is a step toward such standardization, and its use is urged for all private and public Contracts where a statutory form is not prescribed.

Performance Bond. AIA Document A-311—The function of the Performance Bond is to assure the Owner that the Contractor will perform all the terms and conditions of the Contract between him and the Owner and in default thereof to protect the Owner against loss up to the bond penalty. AIA forms of agreement between the Contractor and Owner and between Architect and Owner include provisions for payment to the Architect for the added burden to him in arranging on behalf of the Owner for the work to proceed should the Contractor default. As an element of damage in the agreement between Contractor and Owner, reimbursement to the Owner for such additional fees is covered by this document, which also contains a Labor and Material Payment Bond as a bond separate and distinct from the Performance Bond. The Labor and Material Payment Bond serves the function of protecting the laborers and material men.

Historically, the Performance Bond was the first to be developed. In the course of time, provisions for the payment of labor and material furnished in the prosecution of the work were added to the same form. This type of instrument is generally referred to as a 'Combination Performance and Payment Bond.' Combination Bonds no longer carry the approval of the AIA. The two-bond system, of which AIA Document A-311 is an example, is regarded as greatly superior because the inclusion in one instrument of the obligation for the performance of the Contract and for the payment of laborers and material men has given rise to procedural difficulties in the handling of claims against the bond resulting from the competing interests of the Owner on the one hand and laborers and material men on the other. Under the two-bond pattern, the Surety is enabled to make payment without awaiting a determination as to the Owner's priority. These bonds are issued by the companies as a 'package' and there is no additional premium by reason of the separate Labor and Material Payment Bond.

Labor and Material Bond. AIA Document A-311—The Contractor's bills for labor and materials are guaranteed to be paid by this bond.

Bid Bond In Chapter 10, the Invitation For Bids sets forth a provision for Bid Security in the form of a Bid Bond, certified check, or money order. The following extract from the AIA *Architect's Handbook of Professional Practice,* Chapter 7, September 1963 Edition, sets forth the function of the bid guarantee:

> **Bid Bond. AIA Document A-310**—A function of a Bid Bond is to guarantee, that if awarded the Contract within the time stipulated, the bidder will enter into the Contract and furnish the prescribed Performance, and Labor and Material Payment Bonds. If he fails to do so without justification, there shall be paid to the Owner the difference, not to exceed the penal sum of the bond, between his bid and such larger amount for which the Owner may in good faith contract with another party to perform the work covered by said bid. A Bid Bond does not assure the Owner that he will get a building for the bid price. These are the functions of the Performance, and Labor and Material Payment Bonds.
>
> On private work, the acceptance of a Bid Bond as an alternative to the deposit of a certified check or a bank draft is discretionary with the Owner. In such cases, it is recommended that the bid security be not less than 10% of the amount of the bid, and that this sum should be expressed in words and figures as a specific number of dollars and not as a percentage of the bid. On public work, the amount of the bid security and its form may be specified by law or regulation and such legal requirements will govern.

Guarantee—Warranty Article 4.51 of the AIA General Conditions states that "the Contractor *warrants* and *guarantees* to the Owner and the Architect that all materials and equipment incorporated in the project will be new, and that all work will be of good quality, free from faults and defects and in conformance with the Contract Documents."

Article 4.5.2 of the AIA General Conditions states that "the *warranties* and *guarantees* provided in this paragraph and elsewhere in the Contract Documents shall be in addition to and not in limitation of any other *warranty* or *guarantee* or remedy required by law or by the Contract Documents."

Article 9.3.3 of the AIA General Conditions states that "the Contractor warrants and guarantees that title to all work, materials and equipment, . . . will have passed to the Owner, . . . free and clear of all liens . . . ''

Article 13.2.2 of the AIA General Conditions states that ''if, within one year after the date of Substantial Completion or within such longer period of time as may be prescribed by law or by the terms of any applicable special *guarantee* required by the Contract Documents, any of the work is found to be defective . . . the Contractor shall correct it promptly.''

The reference cited above to ''guarantee'' and ''warranty'' are intended to call attention to two words used in specifications that are often confused, and at no time more confusing than when the specification writer looks up their meanings either in *Webster's Unabridged Dictionary* or in *Black's Law Dictionary*. When one reads all the definitions given in these sources, it may result in the very confusion warned against.

In prior issues of the AIA General Conditions, no references were made to warranties. The current AIA General Conditions includes both terms for materials, workmanship, and ownership of work free of liens. The specifier would be well advised to allow the language used in the AIA General Conditions to stand as written without alternation on his part, leaving to the Owner and the Owner's attorney the onus and responsibility of changing the language of the General Conditions if they so choose.

A warranty is sometimes required in a construction contract in connection with the furnishing of certain materials, products, or equipment. By means of the warranty, the Contractor or manufacturer certifies that the material, product, or equipment will perform as required. A warranty promises performance, and if the warranty is not as stated and if the material, product, or equipment should fail to perform as warranted, the Contractor or manufacturer has committed a breach of contract and the Owner may seek legal recourse for fulfillment of the warranty.

Many manufactured articles are advertised as ''guaranteed'' or ''warranteed.'' The term may mean much or nothing. The Architect should investigate any such guarantee or warranty carefully before specifying materials or equipment so advertised. Sometimes there are ''jokers'' or disclaimers in the printed form.

He should also investigate the reputation and reliability of the concern giving the guarantee or warranty. When guarantees are called for, the Architect should not fail to secure them before accepting the work. He cannot leave this to the surety furnishing the bond, as the surety does not undertake this duty.

The one year guarantee of work set forth in Article 13.2 may not be adequate for certain types of work. It is customary to include special guarantee clauses for such items as waterproofing, roofing, curtain walls, and wood doors, where defective workmanship or materials may result in damages that may not evidence themselves until a longer period of time has elapsed. Where additional protection is desired, the terms of Article 13.2 should be so modified under the appropriate technical Section to provide for a longer guarantee period.

The following examples of guarantee clauses may be used to secure additional protection for defects in materials and workmanship:

1. GUARANTEE

The Contractor hereby guarantees that the membrane waterproofing will be free from defective materials and workmanship for a period of three years after the date of Substantial Completion, as defined in Article 8.1.3 of the AIA General Conditions. Upon notification of any such defects within said guarantee period, the Contractor shall make all necessary repairs and replacements at no cost or expense to the Owner, in accordance with the requirements of Article 13.2 of the AIA General Conditions.

2. GUARANTEE

Prior to final payment, the Contractor shall furnish the Architect with a three-year written guarantee of all work performed and materials furnished for membrane waterproofing. The guarantee shall state that the membrane waterproofing will be free from defective materials and workmanship for a period of three years after the date of Substantial Completion, as defined in Article 8.1.3 of the AIA General Conditions and that the Contractor will make all necessary repairs and replacements at no cost or expense to the Owner. The guarantee shall be in a form satisfactory to the Architect.

3. GUARANTEE

Membrane waterproofing shall be guaranteed against defective materials and workmanship for a period of three years after the date of Substantial Completion, as defined in Article

8.1.3 of the AIA General Conditions. The Contractor shall furnish the Owner with a three year guarantee bond of a Surety Company approved by the Owner, guaranteeing that the Contractor will correct and repair at his own cost and expense any defective material and workmanship in the membrane waterproofing.

Example 1, above, requires no additional written guarantee, since the language states that "the Contractor hereby guarantees" etc., and by his signature to the agreement the contractor has furnished the necessary written guarantee. Simply stating that the work will be guaranteed to be free from defects does not assure the owner that the contractor will remedy any defects that will appear later. The language requiring that the contractor will make good any defects is desirable to bind the contractor to his obligation. Example 2 is used in those instances where the owner or his legal counsel wants the assurance of separate written guarantees. Example 3 is used where the owner or his legal counsel wants still further assurance that a third party will undertake to answer for the performance of another.

The law regarding warranties, guarantees, and guarantors or sureties varies in different states. An owner should secure an opinion from a competent lawyer respecting the wording of any guarantee or warranty forming a part of the specifications, since the specifications are one of the contract documents. The architect should notify the owner of this necessity. The architect may prepare the contract documents, including the agreement, but the legal form should be passed on by a lawyer familiar with the laws relating to building.

THE AMERICAN INSTITUTE OF ARCHITECTS

AIA DOCUMENT
SEPT. 1963 ED.

A311

PERFORMANCE BOND

KNOW ALL MEN BY THESE PRESENTS: that (Here insert name and address or legal title of Contractor)

as Principal, hereinafter called Contractor, and, (Here insert the legal title and address of Surety)

as Surety, hereinafter called Surety, are held and firmly bound unto (Name and address or legal title of Owner)

as Obligee, hereinafter called Owner, in the amount of

Dollars ($),

for the payment whereof Contractor and Surety bind themselves, their heirs, executors, administrators, successors and assigns, jointly and severally, firmly by these presents.

WHEREAS,

Contractor has by written agreement dated   19   , entered into a contract with Owner for

in accordance with drawings and specifications prepared by (Here insert full name, title and address)

which contract is by reference made a part hereof, and is hereinafter referred to as the Contract.

194

NOW, THEREFORE, THE CONDITION OF THIS OBLIGATION is such that, if Contractor shall promptly and faithfully perform said Contract, then this obligation shall be null and void; otherwise it shall remain in full force and effect.

The Surety hereby waives notice of any alteration or extension of time made by the Owner.

Whenever Contractor shall be, and declared by Owner to be in default under the Contract, the Owner having performed Owner's obligations thereunder, the Surety may promptly remedy the default, or shall promptly

1) Complete the Contract in accordance with its terms and conditions, or

2) Obtain a bid or bids for submission to Owner for completing the Contract in accordance with its terms and conditions, and upon determination by Owner and Surety of the lowest responsible bidder, arrange for a contract between such bidder and Owner, and make available as work progresses (even though there should be a default or a succession of defaults under the contract or contracts of completion arranged under this

paragraph) sufficient funds to pay the cost of completion less the balance of the contract price; but not exceeding, including other costs and damages for which the Surety may be liable hereunder, the amount set forth in the first paragraph hereof. The term "balance of the contract price," as used in this paragraph, shall mean the total amount payable by Owner to Contractor under the Contract and any amendments thereto, less the amount properly paid by Owner to Contractor.

Any suit under this bond must be instituted before the expiration of two (2) years from the date on which final payment under the contract falls due.

No right of action shall accrue on this bond to or for the use of any person or corporation other than the Owner named herein or the heirs, executors, administrators or successors of Owner.

Signed and sealed this   day of   A.D. 19

IN THE PRESENCE OF:

_____

_____   _____ (Seal)
                                        (*Principal*)

                                        _____
                                        (*Title*)

_____   _____ (Seal)
                                        (*Surety*)

                                        _____
                                        (*Title*)

PERFORMANCE/LABOR-MATERIAL BOND

LABOR AND MATERIAL PAYMENT BOND

THIS BOND IS ISSUED SIMULTANEOUSLY WITH PERFORMANCE BOND IN FAVOR OF THE
OWNER CONDITIONED ON THE FULL AND FAITHFUL PERFORMANCE OF THE CONTRACT

KNOW ALL MEN BY THESE PRESENTS: that (Here insert name and address or legal title of Contractor)

as Principal, hereinafter called Principal, and, (Here insert the legal title and address of Surety)

as Surety, hereinafter called Surety, are held and firmly bound unto (Name and address or legal title of Owner)

as Obligee, hereinafter called Owner, for the use and benefit of claimants as hereinbelow defined, in the

amount of (Here insert a sum equal to at least one-half of the contract price) Dollars ($),

for the payment whereof Principal and Surety bind themselves, their heirs, executors, administrators, successors and assigns, jointly and severally, firmly by these presents.

WHEREAS,

Principal has by written agreement dated 19 , entered into a contract with Owner for

in accordance with drawings and specifications prepared by (Here insert full name, title and address)

which contract is by reference made a part hereof, and is hereinafter referred to as the Contract.

PERFORMANCE/LABOR-MATERIAL BOND   FOUR PAGES

AIA DOC. A311   SEPT. 1963 ED.

NOW, THEREFORE, THE CONDITION OF THIS OBLIGATION is such that, if Principal shall promptly make payment to all claimants as hereinafter defined, for all labor and material used or reasonably required for use in the performance of the Contract, then this obligation shall be void; otherwise it shall remain in full force and effect, subject, however, to the following conditions:

1. A claimant is defined as one having a direct contract with the Principal or with a subcontractor of the Principal for labor, material, or both, used or reasonably required for use in the performance of the contract, labor and material being construed to include that part of water, gas, power, light, heat, oil, gasoline, telephone service or rental of equipment directly applicable to the Contract.

2. The above named Principal and Surety hereby jointly and severally agree with the Owner that every claimant as herein defined, who has not been paid in full before the expiration of a period of ninety (90) days after the date on which the last of such claimant's work or labor was done or performed, or materials were furnished by such claimant, may sue on this bond for the use of such claimant, prosecute the suit to final judgment for such sum or sums as may be justly due claimant, and have execution thereon. The Owner shall not be liable for the payment of any costs or expenses of any such suit.

3. No suit or action shall be commenced hereunder by any claimant:

a) Unless claimant, other than one having a direct contract with the Principal, shall have given written notice to any two of the following: The Principal, the Owner, or the Surety above named, within ninety (90) days after such claimant did or performed the last of the work or labor, or furnished the last of the materials for which said claim is made, stating with substantial

accuracy the amount claimed and the name of the party to whom the materials were furnished, or for whom the work or labor was done or performed. Such notice shall be served by mailing the same by registered mail or certified mail, postage prepaid, in an envelope addressed to the Principal, Owner or Surety, at any place where an office is regularly maintained for the transaction of business, or served in any manner in which legal process may be served in the state in which the aforesaid project is located, save that such service need not be made by a public officer.

b) After the expiration of one (1) year following the date on which Principal ceased work on said Contract, it being understood, however, that if any limitation embodied in this bond is prohibited by any law controlling the construction hereof such limitation shall be deemed to be amended so as to be equal to the minimum period of limitation permitted by such law.

c) Other than in a state court of competent jurisdiction in and for the county or other political subdivision of the state in which the project, or any part thereof, is situated, or in the United States District Court for the district in which the project, or any part thereof, is situated, and not elsewhere.

4. The amount of this bond shall be reduced by and to the extent of any payment or payments made in good faith hereunder, inclusive of the payment by Surety of mechanics' liens which may be filed of record against said improvement, whether or not claim for the amount of such lien be presented under and against this bond.

Signed and sealed this   day of   A.D. 19

IN THE PRESENCE OF:

_____(Principal)   (Seal)

_____(Title)

_____(Surety)   (Seal)

_____(Title)

197

PERFORMANCE/LABOR-MATERIAL BOND

THE AMERICAN INSTITUTE OF ARCHITECTS

AIA DOCUMENT
SEPT. 1963 ED.

A310

BID BOND

KNOW ALL MEN BY THESE PRESENTS, that we

as Principal, hereinafter called the Principal, and

a corporation duly organized under the laws of the State of
as Surety, hereinafter called the Surety, are held and firmly bound unto

as Obligee, hereinafter called the Obligee, in the sum of

Dollars ($),
for the payment of which sum well and truly to be made, the said Principal and the said Surety, bind ourselves, our heirs, executors, administrators, successors and assigns, jointly and severally, firmly by these presents.

WHEREAS, the Principal has submitted a bid for

NOW, THEREFORE, if the Obligee shall accept the bid of the Principal and the Principal shall enter into a contract with the Obligee in accordance with the terms of such bid, and give such bond or bonds as may be specified in the bidding or contract documents with good and sufficient surety for the faithful performance of such contract and for the prompt payment of labor and material furnished in the prosecution thereof, or in the event of the failure of the Principal to enter such contract and give such bond or bonds, if the Principal shall pay to the Obligee the difference not to exceed the penalty hereof between the amount specified in said bid and such larger amount for which the Obligee may in good faith contract with another party to perform the work covered by said bid, then this obligation shall be null and void, otherwise to remain in full force and effect.

Signed and sealed this   day of   A.D. 19   ,

_____ }

_____ (Seal)
Principal

_____
Title

_____ }

_____ (Seal)
Surety

_____
Title

BID BOND
AIA DOC. A310   SEPT. 1963 ED.   ONE PAGE

17

UNIFORM SYSTEM

With the advent of the CSI Format for Construction Specifications (Chapter 3) it became apparent to both CSI and AIA that this basic framework could be extended into a system for filing product data and to construction cost accounting as well as to a specifications outline.

A Joint Industry Conference Committee, in which many organizations from the United States and Canada participated, evolved this "Uniform System for Construction Specifications, Data Filing, and Cost Accounting, Title One Buildings," which was published in October 1966. The Uniform System combines a specifications outline, a filing system for manufacturer's literature, and a project cost accounting guide, all aligned in a similarity of terms based primarily upon the nomenclature used for the basic section title. The principles established for the product data filing and the cost accounting system contained in the Uniform System are beyond the scope of this book.

The Uniform System creates a preferred terminology for section titles under the CSI Format for Construction Specifications in a recommended sequence. Those who wish to assign a permanent number to all the section titles appearing in the Uniform System for their own use and convenience are at liberty to do so. Others may prefer to assign a number to the section title only when it is used in a project specification. If the former method is employed, any gaps appearing in the section numbers within the table of contents can be clarified by an appropriate note. If the latter method is used, the section title numbers appearing in the table of contents will, of course, be arranged in numerical sequence.

Of particular interest and significance to the specifier is the development within the Specification Outline of two new categories of section titles—the Broadscope Title and the Narrow Scope Title. This arrangement stems from the fact that since a specification section is essentially a unit of work, it may be very broad for one project and encompass many small items, or it may be very narrow in scope for another project and cover in detail a large volume of identical work. This permits the specifier the same flexibility he always enjoyed in the content of his technical section prior to the advent of the CSI Format and the Uniform System.

As an illustration, under Division 2 there is a broadscope section entitled "Clearing of Site," and under it, three narrow-scope sections, entitled "Demolition," "Structures Moving," and "Clearing and Grubbing." If the project were on a small site consisting of a toolshed to be moved, a henhouse to be demolished, and several trees to be cut down, the specifier would determine that this work could very well be written under one broadscope section entitled "Clearing of Site," and describe under appropriate paragraphs within the section each of the items of work to be accomplished. If the project were on a large site consisting of acres of trees and shrubs to be cleared and one major structure to be demolished, the specifier would write two narrow-scope sections, one entitled "Demolition," under which he would describe in detail the demolition of the existing major structure, and under another section entitled "Clearing and Grubbling" he would describe the removal of existing acres of trees and shrubs. In any event, each section title, whether broad-scope or narrow-scope, has all the elements necessary for its stature as an independent section. The determination as to whether the unit of work and, subsequently, the content of the section is to be broad or narrow is determined by the needs of the specific project and the prerogative of the specifier.

The additional text of Part 1—the Specifications Outline is contained in the Uniform System. This document, which is essential to the specifications writer in establishing his section titles for a specific project, may be obtained from either of the following organizations:

American Institute of Architects
1735 New York Avenue N.W.
Washington, D.C. 20006

Construction Specifications Institute
1717 Massachusetts Avenue N.W.
Washington, D.C. 20036

NOTES

Many Section titles are shown in the plural in the Uniform System Specification Outline. These titles should be changed to the singular where project requirements indicate.

Specification Sections may be numbered by the specification writer in any way he prefers. He may choose to use the Uniform System Division number followed by a capital letter identifying each of the several Sections in that Division, "8A" for example. When a fixed numbering system is preferred, use of the four-digit system shown in the Cost Accounting Guide, Uniform System Part 3, is recommended.

The Specification Outline includes both BROADSCOPE and Narrowscope Sections in great variety and number, and the individual project specifications will rarely, if ever, follow Section titles and sequence in every detail. Typical specifications will use only a portion of the titles listed, and some will require the modification of Uniform System Section titles or the introduction of new titles. However, it is recommended that Section titles be selected whenever possible from the comprehensive set shown in Part 1.

Division 1 encompasses certain aspects of project requirements often included in the General Conditions. When the recommendations of Division 1 are followed, the Conditions of the Contract should include appropriate Supplementary Conditions to avoid duplication of material contained in such General Conditions as those published by the American Institute of Architects, the Consulting Engineers Council of the United States, and others.

SUMMARY OF THE WORK	Encompasses summaries of work under this contract, work under other contracts related to the project, work & equipment to be provided by the owner, and work to be postponed to a date later than the designated completion date. It should be clearly stated here whether work is to be completed under a single contract or under several contracts.
SCHEDULES & REPORTS	Encompasses the certification of lines & levels, reference to applicable building standards of such organizations as American Society for Testing & Materials, American Standards Association, American Institute of Steel Construction, American Concrete Institute, and General Services Administration; required inspections; a schedule of required tests; a list of approved testing agencies or criteria for their selection & approval; subsurface soil reports; progress reports & photographs; work progress & critical path schedules; project master color schedule; a glossary of standard abbreviations & symbols; and similar items related to the project as a whole. See 2 EARTHWORK for testing related to soil compaction; 2 PILING for piling tests; 3 CAST-IN-PLACE CONCRETE & 3 PRECAST CONCRETE for testing & inspection of concrete.
SAMPLES & SHOP DRAWINGS	Encompasses procedures for submission of shop drawings & samples. Required shop drawings & samples are normally best specified here in scheduled or tabular form, but it is recommended that a reference to this portion of the Specifications be included in each of the various Sections covering work for which samples or shop drawings are required.
TEMPORARY FACILITIES	Encompasses access roads, barricades & lanterns, construction elevators & hoists, construction stairs, construction offices, storage of tools & equipment, first aid facilities, temporary fences & guardrails, moisture control, parking, runways, scaffolding, staging platforms, signs, site access restrictions, temporary telephone service, outdoor toilet facilities, watchman, and similar provisions necessary to the safe and expeditious progress of the work. This portion of the Specifications normally encompasses the *temporary* provision of electrical power, lighting, space heating, water, or indoor toilet facilities. It is recommended that a reference to this Section be included in each of the other Sections covering similar work of a permanent nature.
CLEANING UP	Encompasses the sweeping, brushing, and other general cleaning of completed work and the removal of debris, surplus material, tools not in active use, and scaffolding & other equipment no longer needed. See various Sections in other Divisions for removal of unwanted material, for initial cleandown of newly installed work, and for cleaning of existing work.
PROJECT CLOSEOUT	Encompasses procedures for delivering guarantees & bonds, for preparing the punchlist, and for final inspection of the project; as-built drawings & specifications required and procedure for their submission; scope & content of the maintenance manual and procedure for its submission; and similar items related to the project as a whole. It is recommended that a reference to this portion of the Specifications be included in each of the various Sections covering work for which as-built drawings & specifications, guarantees, bonds, or maintenance manual data are required.
ALLOWANCES	Tabulates and defines all cash allowances for specified portions of the work. It is recommended that dollar amounts appear only in a master list located here and that reference to this portion of the Specifications be included in each of the various Sections covering work similar to that for which cash allowance is to be made. Cash allowances may also be itemized on the Bid Form.

204

ALTERNATES

Lists all Alternates, describing in complete detail those Alternates that affect the scope of the project and summarizing those Alternates that deal with materials & methods of construction. Further reference to Alternates of project scope normally is limited to the Bid Form, but Alternates of materials & methods must be specified in complete detail in each of the various Sections affected and in brief in the Bid Form. It is essential that the Bid Form list all Alternates, assign a number or other reference designation to each, describe each briefly, and provide space beside each for the bidders' insertion of consequent additions to or deductions from the base bid.

18

ADDENDA

Definition

This last chapter is an appropriate place to discuss Addenda, since by their very nature, addenda are intended as clarifications of previously issued instructions. The dictionary definition of an addendum is "a thing to be added; an addition." Each addendum is a document added to a previously prepared and issued set of contract documents during the bidding period, and becomes a part of the contract documents as defined in AIA General Conditions, Article 1.1.1.

Purpose

In Chapter 10, under the heading of Instructions to Bidders, paragraph five is concerned with the interpretation of documents. The primary purpose of an addendum is to clarify in writing, questions raised by bidders as to the meaning of the drawings and specifications, or to discrepancies or omissions therein, prior to the receipt of bids. In addition, the addendum can be used as the instrument or vehicle by which additional information is made a part of the contract documents. This additional information can take any of the following forms:

1. Correct errors and omissions
2. Clarify ambiguities
3. Add to or reduce the scope of the work
4. Provide additional information that may affect the bid prices
5. Change the time and place for receipt of bids
6. Change the quality of the work
7. Issue additional names of qualified "or equal" products (See Product Approval Standards under Chapter 7, "Specifying Materials").

Language of Addenda

Clarification by addenda of discrepancies, ambiguities, errors, and omissions in the original contract documents should not be in the form of explanations.

They should be precise instructions, using the language previously employed in the documents. For example, if the drawings show asphalt tile and the specification describes vinyl asbestos tile, one of these documents must be changed. If vinyl asbestos is actually required, the addendum should state the drawing on which the information is contained and instruct that the term "asphalt tile" be deleted and the term "vinyl asbestos tile" be inserted. If asphalt tile is actually required, the specification should be altered by the addendum to state that vinyl asbestos tile be deleted and asphalt tile be inserted, together with the appropriate reference to the proper material. In essence, the altered documents should read as original documents.

If there are conflicts on the drawing, in which one detail shows one arrangement and another detail shows another arrangement, delete the inappropriate detail by addendum rather than explain that it is intended that one detail governs over another. Similarly for conflicts within the specifications, delete the inappropriate material by addendum; do not explain that one is preferred or should govern over the other.

Where changes by addendum to a paragraph of the specifications may be misleading or ambiguous, delete the entire paragraph and rewrite it by addendum. The cardinal rule is to use specification language in the addenda by instructions to the contractor rather than by explanation.

Precautions
Do not issue an involved addendum which requires considerable work on the part of bidders unless there is still sufficient time before the bid due date. If time is scant for such a change, alter the bid due date.

Do not clarify a bidder's telephone inquiry verbally. Instruct him to reduce the inquiry to writing and if a clarification is in order, answer it by an addendum to all bidders, so that every bidder is informed through the right channels and there is no misinterpretation of verbal instructions.

A simple change two or three days prior to receipt of bids may be made by telegram; however, the content of the telegraphic addendum should then be transmitted in the form of a formal addendum for the record.

In private work, where changes are negotiated with a successful bidder before award of contract, the changes should be incorporated in the form of an addendum prior to the execution of the agreement or the contract form.

All addenda should be prepared, controlled, and issued by one individual, preferably the specification writer, who has intimate knowledge of all the contract documents and who serves as the clearing house for gathering and arranging all the bits of information. Do not permit consultants, *i.e.,* structural, mechanical and site engineers, to issue addenda, since they may inadvertently assign wrong addenda numbers or issue instructions that conflict with other instructions contained elsewhere in the contract documents.

Itemize each instruction or change within the addendum by a number for future reference during construction and correspondence. (See illustration of Sample Addendum.)

Format of Addenda

Each addendum should be arranged in an orderly sequence. Changes to the Project Manual (book of specifications) should follow the sequence of the table of contents, after the introductory statements as follows:

Introduction
1. Name of Architect, Engineer, or Issuing Agency
2. Project Identification
3. Addendum Number
4. Date of Addendum
5. Opening Remarks and Instructions (See Sample Addendum)

Sequence of Addendum Changes
1. Changes to Prior Addenda
2. Changes to Table of Contents
3. Changes to Invitation to Bid
4. Changes to Instructions to Bidders
5. Changes to Bid Form
    Note: Reissue separate pages of the Bid Form requiring changes.
6. Changes to Contract Forms
7. Changes to General and Supplementary Conditions
8. Changes to Specification Sections—in sequence
9. Changes to Drawings—in sequence

SAMPLE ADDENDUM

JOHN JONES, ARCHITECT
123 MAIN STREET
NEW YORK, NEW YORK

LIBRARY BUILDING
FIRST AVENUE & MAIN STREET
NEW YORK, NEW YORK

ADDENDUM NO. 2
JANUARY 10, 1967

The original specifications and drawings, dated January 1, 1967, for the above-noted project are amended as noted in this Addendum No. 2.

Receipt of this Addendum shall be acknowledged by inserting its number and date in the space provided on the Bid Form.

This Addendum consists of _____ pages, (and the attachments noted herein).

ITEM NO.   ADDENDUM NO. 1
ADD 2-1   Item No. ADD 1-3. Add the following: "Mirrors shall be Model A as manufactured by XYZ Company."

BID FORM
ADD 2-2   *Delete Page BID-3 bound in the specifications dated January 1, 1967. The attached page BID-3 (REVISED, AD-DENDUM NO. 2) shall be used by all Bidders.

SPECIFICATIONS
SECTION 4A, UNIT MASONRY
ADD 2-3   Page 4A-2, Par. 4A.3.b., Line 2, Change "$60/M cash allowance" to "$80/M cash allowance."

SECTION 9A, RESILIENT FLOORING
ADD 2-4   Page 9A-5, Par. 9A.7.c.1., Delete last sentence.

DRAWINGS
DRAWING A-3
ADD 2-5   Room 302. Change flooring from "terrazzo" to "asphalt tile."

*Changes in bid form should be made by reissuing the specific page requiring a change. This is in keeping with the rule that the format of the bid form is best prepared by the architect.

ACKNOWLEDGMENT

Chapter 11, pages 90-127. The insurance terms listed are from the Construction Specifications Institute study entitled "Supplementary General Conditions" dated April 1964, pages 59 and 60.

INDEX

214